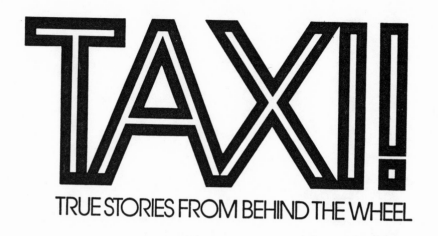

TAXI!

TRUE STORIES FROM BEHIND THE WHEEL

JOHN JOHNSON

MACMILLAN OF CANADA / TORONTO

Canadian Cataloguing in Publication Data

Johnson, John, 1925-
  Taxi!

ISBN 0-7705-1654-8

1. Johnson, John, 1925-   2. Taxicab drivers—Ontario—Toronto—
Anecdotes, facetiae, satire, etc. I. Title.

HE5635.T67J64   388.4′1321′0207   C78-001050-7

*The writing of this book was assisted by an Ontario Arts Council
Grant, for which I am grateful. J.J.*

Printed in Canada for
The Macmillan Company of Canada Limited
70 Bond Street, Toronto
M5B 1X3

FOR DEIRDRE
who always wanted me out of the business

and for all my buddies
who are still in it.

☞ CONTENTS

ix FOREWORD
 1 PROLOGUE
 3 ONE-EYED JACK IS WILD
 7 THE LAST PHILOSOPHERS?
11 SOME PEOPLE GOT NO CLASS
15 DUST IN THE RAIN
19 LOAD LIMIT
25 IN CASE YOU WONDERED WHERE I WAS...
29 THE PURSE
31 WHAT'S A NICE GIRL LIKE YOU...
37 COLLECTOR'S COLUMN
43 PAINS—THIRTY SECONDS
47 THE NIGHT THE GREEK SMILED
53 NOTHING EXCEEDS LIKE EXCESS
59 THE WORD OF A LADY
63 THE LOSERS
69 MY OLD MAN WOULD'VE KILLED ME
73 THE SHOT-GLASS JUNGLE
81 CAPTAIN JACK AND THE LITTLE PEOPLE
87 THE GOLD SHIRT
91 SOMETHING TO THINK ABOUT...
95 BIOLOGY II
99 BRING ON THE CLOWNS
105 A LONELY WAY TO DIE

111 THE NIGHT CHARLIE GOT THE BLOOD
115 TOUGH GUY
119 THE GIRLS
127 ACCOUNT PAYABLE
133 "YOU'RE NEVER ALONE..."
137 LAW 'N' ORDER
141 CONTRIBUTOR'S CORNER
143 YOU WIN ONE WHEN YOU CAN
149 THE HOMECOMING
155 FALSE START
159 PSYCHO WARD
169 CAST OF CHARACTERS
179 ROYALTY
185 SUPERMAN AND THE TREELOADER
189 ONE SHOE
193 THE TIME HARRY DIDN'T PAY THE RENT
197 LEGAL EAGLE
205 FOR SERVICES RENDERED
209 ALL IT TAKES IS A PHONE CALL
215 COPS AND ROBBERS
223 EPILOGUE

 FOREWORD

It has been observed that every function of which the human body is capable—every one—has been performed, at one time or another, in the back seat of a taxi.

In the course of a single shift a driver will meet between thirty and a hundred total strangers: all shapes, all sizes, with and without warts. These meetings will take place within a volume of space roughly one-third that of a very small bathroom, which tends to lend an intimacy that would be wildly out of place in almost any other buy-and-sell encounter. You don't tell your troubles to the shoe-clerk.

There is simply no reason for the driver to expect that all these strangers, hundreds every week, will pass through his life without incident. Given the nature of the business and of its most *usual* clientele—stockbrokers' and millionaires' wives don't count; they seldom take cabs, and then only when the Mercedes is in the shop for service — the odds are vastly against the driver's day being merely a matter of driving people from here to there.

Oh, sure; it can go like that for days, sometimes even weeks, but sooner or later there'll come the petty arrogance, the crafty indignation of the drunk, the bad smells, and the garbage on the floor. Or worse, much worse. Because it's a *people* business, and people are still the most interesting (if sometimes the most infuriating) things aboard this spaceship we call a city. It can be fairly said, I think, that urbanity and delicacy of deportment are not the things that the driver is most likely to remember about the people who filled his day or week or year. Not if he's been paying attention, they're not. It probably works both ways.

This book had to be written. Not because the world needed a social document about cab-drivers and cab-passengers; it's been done before, for one thing—but seldom by anyone *in* the business, behind the wheel. Damon Runyon and others (including the writer of that remarkable film that circulated a year or two ago) wrote about characters who just *happened* to be taxi drivers; they could just as easily have been about almost *anyone* who talked and thought in the language of the street. The job was completely secondary to the character.

This book, on the other hand, came from reflections in the rear-view mirror, from whispered conversations in the back seat—and from my own, often burdensome, sense of the ridiculous.

That sense of the ridiculous — far too finely honed, perhaps; some of my buddies tell me *nothing* ever happens in *their* cabs—persuaded me, finally, that the whole damned thing had to be put down on paper. It all started with one of the shortest stories in the book: *Dust in the Ruin*. Over the next three or four years, still driving, I wrote perhaps another half-dozen of the stories that appear here. Several others remain forever condemned to the back of the desk drawer.

It didn't start to become a book, not really, until about nine months ago — and I swear there's no symbolism there. Honest. Anyway, I came to the point of: "Why the hell not?" and Doug Gibson, editorial director for Macmillan's, saw what I was trying to do. I can never thank him enough for his help and encouragement; and I'll sure as hell never forgive him for failing to tell me what a solitary, lonely chore the whole damned thing would become by the time it was finished. But, I guess we grow with these things: the sound of traffic at three a.m. has a beauty all its own, and a rhythm that makes the mental juices flow, somehow. These traffic sounds—even through my apartment window—brought the whole taxi scene back to life for me; they made me recall stories, good stories, that I'd almost forgotten even while they'd been happening.

Did all the stories in this book *really* happen? Well, let me put it this way:

Yes. Absolutely. In fact, some of them are *understated*. The first-person stories were written directly from my own experience, just about precisely as they happened, granting — if you will — possible inaccuracies in dialogue; some of them took place five or six years ago. Many of the other stories are written in the third person, for dramatic effect; some of them happened to me, some didn't. A story about Joe may have actually concerned Bill; it doesn't matter. A few names have been changed to protect the guilty (Glickman and Rosie are invented names, for example); a few others are really composites. *The Homecoming,* for instance, was written as if only three principal characters were involved; actually, there were *four.* But it *did* happen, and there *was* a .38 revolver sitting in someone's lap. It happened. All the stories happened.

Let me say this: I never went looking for trouble, never. Not one time. I managed to find my share, though. And I have this hunch that a lot of the guys pay so little attention to what's happening that potential trouble just peters out before they notice. I've often wished I had that faculty.

Finally, a caution to my cab-driving friends:

However strongly you may find yourself identifying with a particular story, don't try to find yourself in it; chances are, you're just not there. Or, worse, you're a composite — and who in hell wants to be one of those?

There are a few exceptions: the Stoddart killing did happen, and the victim's name *was* Stoddart. The Kafka-esque "Inspection Office" is a thinly disguised name for an arm of government we all fear and suspect — needing only a good blast of insecticide to bring it to probable ruin. And Jay (his real name) *did* wear a pink bunny suit on Easter weekend. And Chris *does* have chestnut hair. Yes, indeed.

> John Johnson
> Toronto
> November, 1977

TAXI!

PROLOGUE

☛ "You don't look like a cab-driver," said the lady in the back seat.

No, said the cab-driver.

"I mean, I always thought cab-drivers were . . . well, I mean . . . you know, sort of . . ." said the lady in the back seat.

Yes and no, said the cab-driver.

"Well, do you do this all the time?" the lady asked. "Is this your living?"

There is no time, the driver said; I have no living.

"I don't understand," the lady complained.

It is very simple, he told her; I am merely an apparition, a figment of the imagination.

"But that's ridiculous!" the lady protested.

Not at all, said the driver, it's quite normal; it is the way we operate.

"How can that be?" the lady asked.

Simplicity itself, the driver told her; when you phone for a taxi, our dispatcher causes a car and a driver to be created, on the instant, right at your door.

"Really, now!" exclaimed the lady in the back seat.

It's true, the cab-driver told her, some people think it happens in a puff of smoke or a flash of brimstone, but it's not that dramatic; we are created, so to speak, out of thin air, and you have only to wish it.

"What happens then?" asked the lady.

It is happening now, said the driver; you are whisked to your destination and the very purpose of my existence is fulfilled.

"And after that?" the lady asked.

I return to the place whence I came and there is nothing more, the driver told her.

"I don't believe you," said the lady in the back seat.

No, said the cab-driver.

When the lady had left the cab and closed the door behind her, she did not turn to see if it was still there.

# ONE-EYED JACK IS WILD

☛ Why does half my trouble come boogie-ing out of a gas station? Damned if I know, but it's unreal. This time it was a Sunoco.

I remember wondering why this dude was standing outside in the dark, rather than waiting inside the station office; it was as cold as a bailiff's conscience. He'd probably borrowed the phone to call us, so why wait outside? I stopped the car with the right front door centred at his belt-buckle; most guys ride in the front. He climbed into the back, and there are times when you wonder if that's a good sign. And I remember checking the jacket: a dark-blue uniform-type with "Jack" embroidered over the right breast pocket. I didn't quite make the company logo on the other side, but it wasn't the Sunoco flash.

Blacks aren't usually uptight. I didn't say they're friendly—they don't owe us that—it's more like: "So okay, man, we got this ofay cat workin' for *us* for a change, and that's only cool." No problem. We take the people where they want to go. Yessir.

This was different. I know how to talk to people; it's part of my trade. You come on to me with three purple heads, and there's a good chance I'll think of something to say that shouldn't bother you. But not with Jack. Nothing worked; nothing. It was a half-hour ride, and you learn to feel tension coming from the back seat; sometimes it's like a kick under the heart. This was one of those times.

I tried to get a good look at him in the rear-view: big, maybe twenty—and nervous. That's all I could read. And why nervous? I don't think it was my driving; most people seem to relax okay. Maybe it tied in with the address he'd given me. A fairly shitty part of town. A couple of alarms rang in my head when he suddenly told me to pull up a few blocks short of there, right at the mouth of a dark, ratty-looking alley.

Hell, you can't jump at every shadow. I cranked the meter to the "Stop" position and picked up the clipboard to write down the fare, while I waited for him to fumble for his money. About this clipboard: it's made of steel rather than fibre, with a piano-hinged lid. It weighs about two pounds, and I'd often wondered why the boss bothered with such an elaborate damned thing rather than a ninety-eight-cent job from Woolworth's. Nothing important ever got written on it.

Nine dollars and ten cents. The time was eight thirty-five.

I have to explain something: this town gets bigger and nastier. And sudden movement in a cab is like a trigger—you can't just sit there. It pays to learn fast.

Something flashed in the corner of my eye, something coming over the seat back. I don't know why the hell I did it; the flash could have been a handful of quarters for the fare. The steel clipboard was in my right hand, closed, the trip already written in. Without really thinking, I swung that sonofabitch with everything I had, around and over my right shoulder until I felt it bite.

Jack let out a bellow of pain and outrage and I turned just as he put his hands to his face. I caught a glimpse of a red, welling mess just about where one of his eyes should have been. He roared something I didn't quite catch, then bolted from the car like he was on rockets—up that god-damned alley.

I felt something heavy kind of leaning against my right thigh; I fumbled for it and brought it up to where the dome light glinted along the mean, honed edge of the five-inch blade. I thought something stupid, like: *That bastard! He could've ripped my new slacks! And he owes me nine bucks* . . .

I piled out of the car and started up the alley. The sounds of my shoes slapping on the pavement rang from the walls of the adjoining buildings.

I'd gone maybe fifty feet when it hit me: "Holy shit! So now you're an alley fighter? Get your ass the hell out of here!" I didn't have to tell myself twice. I got out of there; I damn near scattered the transmission getting out of there.

I tried to raise the dispatcher, but this part of town had always been a dead spot on our radio frequency — which was one reason we'd never been all that keen on business to or from the area. So I looked for a cop car. I swear I drove ten miles, looking for a cop car. Nothing. And here's a hint: if you plan any heavy action, make it a Saturday night — the cops are so busy with the Drinking Irish and the Smoking Teenies and the Drinking Irish and the milk-store heists and the Drinking Irish that they won't even notice what you're doing. Anyway, I gave up looking.

I pulled into a parking lot, turned on the dome light, and checked the back seat for blood. A little less than I'd expected — but enough. More than enough. It was then that I realized exactly what the hell had happened, and the shakes started; I could've caused earthquakes. I figured out that what I'd seen coming over the seat back hadn't really been a stabbing motion — I'd be dead if it had been — but there's not the slightest goddam doubt in the world that that muthuh was going to hold the blade on me till he got my money. Or more.

The bit with the clipboard had been foolhardy. Crazy. But so help me, by the time I'd thought about it — it was done. I smoked for a while, waiting for everything to come down a bit. Then I checked the knife again: it was no gem. Lousy balance, cheap steel, strictly for an amateur. But I'll tell you one thing — that sucker was honed to an edge that could shave a gnat. Close.

I don't know if I *really* peeled his eye out. I hope I didn't; partly because he was an amateur, I guess. But I hope it hurt like everlasting shit. I hope it hurt for a long time. I hope it drove Jack wild.

Aloud, to myself, I said: "That young motherfucker *needed* a lesson." My voice still shook. Just a bit.

 # THE LAST PHILOSOPHERS?

☛ For no good reason, the look of the place reminded me how damned early it really was. It was a big house. Every downstairs light was on, and the white glare of the porch light stung my eyes a little. Against fifty dark houses on the street, it looked almost immoral. Obviously this was a man who saw no need to sneak out of his own house like a burglar, no matter how uncivilized the hour.

He settled into the back seat, carefully arranging his two attaché cases beside him with somewhat the same motions he might have used to help an elegant woman adjust her mink about her shoulders. A strange, fussy gesture — and *two* attaché cases? Must be a heavy-duty trip.

There was nothing fussy about the voice: "Five o'clock on the nose. Good."

"We try, sir." I knew where he was going, but the airport is a big place. "Which terminal?"

"Terminal One. Eastern."

I caught a better look at him as I craned my neck to back the car out of the driveway: senior-executive type. Three-hundred-dollar suit. Florida tan, recent. A bland, intelligent face, like a thousand other airport faces at five in the morning. I decided that his mortgage probably didn't make him nervous.

I like the feeling of the Freeway at this hour. The timid little Toyotas haven't begun to complicate things, and the big tractor rigs set a nice sixty-mile-an-hour pace. I settled into the rhythm of it, a bit smug, knowing that my first trip of the day would put almost twenty dollars on the run-sheet; a good edge on the rest of the shift. I knew my fare would talk when he felt like it. I made a smooth lane-change, fitting us neatly into the slightly faster flow of traffic to the left of the big trucks.

"You enjoy driving, don't you?" The voice from the back seat was a little warmer than I'd expected.

"Yeah. Yeah, I guess I do. How can you tell?"

"Well, for one thing, you're not mad at the car. And you haven't always done this for a living."

"No, I have not. . . ." (Goddam it, there it was again: nobody has *always* driven hack for a living. What the hell is a *real* driver supposed to look and act like — a lardy, smart-assed oaf bred for nothing else?) I must've sounded pretty defensive.

"Relax. I wasn't putting you down."

I don't depend on tips. They're nice to get, and I suppose the reasoning behind them shouldn't really matter, but a tip isn't always a way of saying "Thanks". Some fares have a way of making it almost an insult. Still, I'm greedy enough that I started wondering if I'd blown this one.

There was no more talk for a few minutes, and the next time he spoke it was a complete change of subject. (I think we talked about inflation and the oil companies, but it was a long time ago and I can't be sure.) Anyway, we got along just great for the rest of the half-hour trip. As we pulled up to the Eastern Airlines door he said:

"Y' know . . . you fellows are the last philosophers."

"Philosophers?"

"Sure. Who else can afford to think the way you guys do? Plumbers . . . doctors . . . *me*? I could try, but I'm thirty years out of the habit."

"I still don't see . . ."

"Okay. You have something the rest of us hardly even know we've lost. No one can make you trade off any of your integrity . . . unless you want to. There aren't that kind of carrots in your trade.

You see everything. And you have the time to put it in perspective."

"You seem to know a lot about it."

"I should. I drove cab nights, to put myself through law school. And I kept it up for almost a year after I graduated, waiting for the money to start coming in. The Law Society found out and tried to break my ass for it, but I beat that. So I know something about bullshit and harassment. Good luck!"

The meter read eighteen-sixty; a twenty and a five lay on the seat beside me. I looked up: he was gone.

Philosophers?

Hell, we've got carpenters, poets, guys laid off from General Motors, ex-insurance agents with ulcers like dinner plates, the underemployed from just about every line of work there is . . . and more than our share of semi-professional horse-players. Winners, losers, men who can't wait to get out of the business. And others who can't imagine doing anything else for a living.

You ask: "Why would *anyone* want to spend his life in an underpaid, 'nothing' job like driving a taxi?"

Good question.

This world, obviously, is built for those who ache for the shiny things: a Cadillac, a trip to Spain, whatever. And to hell with the price. The real winners join the parade somewhere about age five, and spend the next fifty years pushing their way to the front. But there are always some who wonder how much sweat and compromise the bright toys are worth, and the answer keeps ducking around the next corner and out of sight. By the time you find it, the answer may have taken the form of a coronary, or a messy divorce, or just the simple process of being laid off from a job you liked. And the dream is lost.

What do you do with a man who will no longer scramble for the goodies? You might as well let him drive a cab. He may piss in your eye, but at least he won't be your responsibility.

I wouldn't want to give you the idea that we're all loaded with intellectual honesty and disdain for the consumer society; that's bullshit. We all *fell* into the business—against our will, mostly—and stayed because we got hooked on the freedom.

Freedom? Sure.

You take a car out at the start of your shift, and you're on your own. Completely. If you hear from your boss more than once a week, you're working for the wrong guy. If business is good you'll make adequate money—and so will he. If it's not, well, tomorrow's another day; nobody is likely to bug you about it. (I once drove for a man for eight months without ever finding out what he looked like. Think about that—the next time your boss calls you in for a little talk.)

Maybe I oversimplify; maybe the freedom isn't all that evident to some of the guys in the trade, or all that important to others. But nobody was ever born behind the wheel of a taxi, and no kid ever grew up dreaming about some day being a cab-driver. Then why do so few of us, once given a good taste of the game, ever *really* leave it? It's not the money—and it sure as hell can't be the sixty-hour weeks.

There's this funny kind of mental adjustment, a couple of things you learn about yourself, after a year or two in the business. You weren't going to be rich anyway—no matter what you did for a living—and somehow it doesn't matter a damn. Nothing really shocks you any more. And the people who pass through your car—friendly, hostile, indifferent, or just drunk—are the stuff of a thousand psychology books.

I think my friend with the two attaché cases was reaching a bit. Philosophers? Hell, no. We're just working stiffs with the heat off. Detachment isn't always wisdom; it can just as easily reflect a kind of permanent adolescence.

☞ SOME PEOPLE GOT NO CLASS

☞ I am not a prude. No. Believe that. Nor do I run around like a rutting moose. I like to learn *who* they are before I concern myself with *how* they are. It has always seemed to me that haste and furtiveness kill most of whatever the act of love is supposed to be all about, and they're a sure-fire way of seeing to it that you both wake up the next morning feeling vaguely insulted. But I guess that doesn't matter to some people.

And back seats are for kids who don't have any place to go; or for adults who can't wait ten minutes. (I'll never understand that; often, those few minutes of waiting are just about the best part of it.) Anyway, some people just got no class. But I'm not a prude.

Another thing I'm not is a voyeur, and I sure as hell don't like to listen. You can close your eyes and not see; but how do you close your ears?

They'd been in the car maybe thirty seconds when the whisperings became fumblings, and then came the rustling of clothing. I don't know how you learn to recognize these sounds; you just do. And the air in the car took on a pungent warmth that had nothing to do with two people sitting a couple of feet apart, just going for a taxi ride. Okay so far. These things happen, although these two seemed just a few years too old for back-seat gropings.

I guess I finally caught on when I pulled up to wait for a stop-light; the car began to rock on the springs, gently, in that rhythm that's just a little older than time. I don't want to get clinical

11

about this, but I'll tell you: the trip lasted about fifteen minutes, and she whooped and moaned and hollered through at least ten minutes of it. He must've been a hell of a man. At one point her head was on the seat back, rolling from side to side as if she was going into some kind of seizure, about three inches from my right shoulder. After a few seconds of that, her head disappeared behind the seat and the moaning and thumping got louder.

Have you ever had the feeling you don't really exist? To these two I was just a part of the machinery, I guess. But maybe not. I've heard of people who can't get off without a dog watching; maybe they needed a cab-driver listening. There are times when you don't know whether to shit or paint houses — and this was one of them. Should I have stopped the car and ordered them out? Assuming they'd even *hear* me, what would that prove? Am I some kind of guardian of the public morals? Not bloody likely. I decided that my own embarrassment was irrelevant, and the name of the game was to keep on driving. Maybe I *was* just part of the machinery, after all.

I'll give them this: their timing was beautiful. Her high, thin wail of completion blended with the small squeal of the brakes as I pulled to a stop in front of the address he'd given me. Within seconds it was evident that his mission was accomplished, too. I'm used to just about anything, but this was just a bit much. I was relieved when the back door cracked open and a sawbuck came drifting over the seat back like a falling leaf.

There were the final, tiny sounds of fabric being smoothed and straightened, quiet murmurings before they got out of the car. I watched them walk toward the doors of the apartment building; not close, not holding hands or anything. And I wondered about that— until I remembered that this hadn't been a class operation from the beginning. Anyway, I wrote up the trip-sheet and gave the back seat a quick glance (just like we're supposed to) in case a purse or something had been left behind. I guess I didn't look closely enough.

My next fare flagged me down within a couple of blocks; a big guy, happily whaled, about thirty. I took dim notice of the fact that he climbed into the back rather than the front; he must've been a business type, although he didn't really look it. Before I could douse the dome light and crank the meter to the "Go" position, he pointed to the back floor and said, "Yecchh!" I leaned over to see what was bothering him.

Problem:

Assuming you hadn't been involved, how in hell would you go about getting a freshly used condom out of the back of your car?

 DUST IN THE RAIN

☛ Three in the morning, Tuesday, October—and raining.

It has rained for five days, a ceaseless drizzle punctuated by heavier stuff drumming in brief surges on the roof of the car. The whip antenna moans up and down through some alien scale, softly, vibrating in the squalls that sweep the rain in patches along the pavement. The red Vic Tanny sign across the street flashes at precise two-second intervals, looking like a neon amoeba through the watery glop on the windshield.

The drunks, indignant and reluctant, have all been ferried home; the night people have finished their furtive errands, and the silence on the radio is thick enough to squeeze in your fist. You've been sitting here... how long? Forty minutes... forty minutes since your last run. A cop car shoots past, heading east at about seventy, roof light flashing, no siren.

Vic Tanny is still across the street, reminding you. (Two-second intervals? *Precise* two-second intervals? Sure. What the hell *else* is there to count?) Your mind starts to play cute games: why not a word that means rain and silence at the same time? Rainlence. . . . Silain. . . .

Shit.

That train of thought is broken, thank God, by the crackle of the radio — the dispatcher's talking to one of the cars downtown — it must be the first real sound you've heard in half an hour. He erupts in

a sharp burst of laughter, and you wish you'd heard the joke.
There's a dim rush of static, then silence again.

As if motion would bring the world back to life, you start the car
and ease into the street, going anywhere. A forgotten tune plays in
your mind to the rhythm of the wipers; another sound, cool and
hypnotic: the whisper of your tires on the wet pavement. Hypnotic, Hypnosis, Hypnotize... Could a person be hypnotized into
ramming a bridge abutment, or whatever? (This car will self-
destruct in five seconds....)

Jeezus!

When you start to think like this, it's time for a coffee and the
Donut Hole is on the next corner. The sudden rush to your bladder
—all the coffee you've drunk this night—kills that thought with a
sharp finality; you drive past the oasis of light and noise. The
agony will pass because it always does, and you know with an odd
perversity that you won't get out of the car for a while yet. But
you're certainly awake now.

As if he knew, the dispatcher calls your number and asks where
you are. Then, "Get the Emergency door."

"Right."

Your thoughts change direction with the car as you thread your
way through the back streets to the hospital, and you wonder what
the hell *this* one is all about. There's a pattern to hospital runs at this
time of night: usually, they've done something very foolish—more
often than not, they live in government housing. It's almost as if the
more affluent arrange to break their bones or take their overdoses or
do their dying within proper office hours.

Sure enough, there's a police car at the Emergency door, lights
and engine off. It's a safe bet your fare arrived in the cruiser.

Before you can get out of the car, the hospital doors swing open
and you fumble with the rear handle, leaning over the seat back
almost to the hernia point. The four of them ease into the cab: a boy
and a girl, fifteen-sixteen, looking alike—and two adults who must
be the parents. The father murmurs an address. All four seem to be
in shock.

The silence hangs in the car like a curtain, and it's no time for conversation. The drumming on the roof becomes more insistent as you wait for a traffic-light to change. The girl's thin face reflects in the rear-view mirror, and her pallor is almost luminous. You wonder if you've ever seen anyone so vulnerable. The wet shimmer on the pavement turns from red to green, and you pull away from the intersection a bit more gently than usual.

It's a ten-minute ride. You turn into the driveway of a solid house in a neighbourhood that is just beginning to show its age. Respectable. And somehow dusty looking, even in the rain.

"Two-ninety, please." Your voice sounds like someone else's.

As they leave the car and start up the walk, the girl steadies herself hand-over-hand along the fender. It's then that you notice the thick bandages on both her wrists.

You wait a second or two before backing out of the driveway slowly, as if any sudden movement could shatter this fragile thing she tried to leave. At fifteen, dear God. And why in hell were you wondering about suicide twenty minutes ago?

You thank whatever Fates let your own kids grow up goofy and healthy and happy. It'll be time to go home, soon. You'll look in on them, sleeping. Just for a minute.

# LOAD LIMIT

☛ I yield to no man in my appreciation of the grape; but I think I'd cheerfully give it up if someone could guarantee — absolutely — that no mouthy, mindless animal would ever again vomit down the back of my neck.

Drunks are a fact of life in the taxi business, and a source of a good chunk of the average driver's income. Drunks can be funny — if you can keep your objectivity and stay about ten yards away from them. But a taxi contains less air space than two phone booths, and a belching, belligerent fool (or two) in the back seat doesn't usually provide much in the way of detached amusement. Even if he's not hostile, you have a tendency to drive like hell and try to get him home before he throws up. Or bores you to death.

It isn't up to me to sermonize, of course — and I've been known to take on more than I should have, from time to time — but I can't help wondering:

Given the likelihood that this country has some of the world's dumbest drinking laws, and the certainty that our booze taxes must be the envy of two-bit politicians everywhere — do we, or do we not, have one of the more spectacular *per capita* drunk problems on earth? If we do (and it's hard to imagine our glorious leaders admitting it), is there a causal effect between the law and the problem?

No politician will ever ask a cab-driver's opinion on the matter — even though we clean up a lot more of the mess than the police ever get around to—but enough of that. A brief, abridged catalogue of drunk types might be useful at this point.

☞ Your average, garden-variety specimen will be the Happy Drunk: a few with the guys after the sales meeting, or maybe after bowling. A night on the town. He couldn't cause trouble if he tried. "Hey, man! Wha's happenin'? Ooh, shit, am I whaled! Whazza time? One? Christ, she'll kill me. Le's go, my good man. I shall see that you are suitably (urp!) comp... compen... rewarded. Drive on!"

All you have to hope is that he stays awake.

☞ Female drunks seldom fall into the Happy Drunk category, perhaps because no woman ever ran down to the local to have a few with the girls, just for something to do. A Happy Drunk gets that way just for the hell of it; a woman gets drunk for a Reason. It's too bad. Hoisting a few should be a pleasure, not a project.

It can get a bit awesome because when they get *really* swacked —and it's usually out of regret, disillusionment, or rage—they can be pure, absolute trouble. And none of the standard drunk-handling techniques work, not even a little bit. A woman who is furious with one man is at war with *all* men, and the driver is a handy target.

☞ And then there's the Crafty Drunk:

"Look, buddy, I know all about you guys... you're all a bunch of goddam thieves. Well, you're not takin' *me* on no fuckin' tour, unnerstan'?"

(God, another one of these!) "Oh, I wouldn't do *that*, sir. Which way d'you want to go?"

"Nev' mind that smart-ass crap. I'll tell you which way we're gonna go...."

"Okay. So tell me."

"I know all about you guys.... I been around."

"You going to tell me, or what?"

"Oh. Yeah. Well, we're goin' up to the highway, across to the valley parkway and down to the lakeshore. I'll tell you from there."

It's miles out of the way from the address he gave at first. "You sure you want to go that way?"

"Look. You jus' keep drivin' like I told you. I know all about you guys. . . . I'll be watchin' you."

Please God, yes. All I need is a mouthy bastard like this to fall asleep halfway there. "Okay. It's your money." The rest isn't hard to guess: we took the long way, exactly as he'd laid it out, and the meter read almost eighteen dollars when we pulled up at his place.

He had to get in the last word: "See? What'd I tell you? I know all about you guys. . . . Bloody good thing I tol' ya how to get here . . . an' I was watchin' all the time. Guess I showed *you*, huh?"

Yep. Sure did. The short way would've cost him about ten.

☛ Of all the drunks who inhabit the back seats of taxis—and I may have missed a few during my years in the game—the Sleeper is the most expensive.

If you can accept the proposition that Time is Money (nobody in this business makes a dime unless the meter is ticking), you'll understand the driver's frustration when, just as he pulls up at his passenger's address, he finds that his fare has lapsed into a coma. There is nothing deeper and more rock-like than the sleep of a thoroughly blasted drunk; it poses a dilemma of some proportions.

The driver has to have his money. Will he:

1) Take his ten dollars (or whatever) from his passenger's wallet—and leave him lying on the front lawn?
2) Hammer on the door of the house and awaken the wife?
3) Call the cops?
4) Forget the whole scene and drive away?

Take your pick; but keep a couple of things in mind:

When your fare is that drunk, it's probably payday—and he'll be sober in the morning. He'll remember how much money he started out with, but he'll forget that he blew fifty of it in some bar. Nobody likes to claim full responsibility for his own disasters (especially a disaster like being dumped, unconscious, on the lawn), and his wife's suggestion that he might have been rolled by some vicious cab-driver will be an excuse he can live with till the next time. And you're not that hard to trace, not really, if he decides to push it.

Hammering on the door and waking his wife is only slightly less dangerous: when father comes home smashed, *all* men become the enemy. There's no point in trying to explain that you're just the poor slob who brought the body home; somewhere in there, it's *your* fault. Believe it.

Call the cops? It's a last, desperate measure, and there's a limit to what they can do. A smart, experienced cop might get your ten dollars for you eventually, but it could take an hour. And, like I said, Time is Money.

The one alternative we haven't considered, of course, is giving the sodden idiot a good rap in the teeth to smarten him up. Not recommended. They all have to sober up some time, and a good lawyer can spike a cab-driver's hide to the courthouse wall without working up a sweat. Assault will be the charge—and the judge may have never seen a drunk in full belch. (Except, of course, at the Granite Club; and after all . . .)

☛ There are other sub-types of drunk, of course. Some are quietly arrogant, others want to be your pal for life. A very few are dangerous, depending on what they've been popping to help the booze along. But most drunks fall into that vague, in-between category that makes a driver wonder what the hell he's doing with his life, playing nursemaid to a bunch of slobbering, glassy-eyed clowns who should know better.

Once, during a conference that involved me, my drooling fare, and a couple of cops—I got the word:

One of the cops took me aside and said, "I know just how you feel, Mac. But look at it this way: *we* can't take 'em all home, and they sure as shit can't be just left where they fall. It's part of the game. If *you* don't clean up the mess, who in hell will?"

He had a point.

☞ IN CASE
YOU WONDERED
WHERE I WAS...

☛ Ten in the morning is an unlikely time for drama, but you never know. It's certainly one of the rush hours in this business: most of the liquor stores open at ten.

Some people have developed their drinking to such a high art that they can finish the old bottle just as a new one becomes available. The morning booze shuttle usually passes without incident; except, perhaps, for the frightened dignity of a man with nothing to do but drink away the first real lay-off of his life—or the sad spectacle of a mink-coated housewife pretending she's just running over to pick up the stuff for her husband's poker game tonight. (You took her to the liquor store yesterday. And the day before yesterday, and the day before that; always at opening time. She won't remember you.)

But this one is different. You can feel trouble as soon as they come out of the house.

He's about thirty, burly. Slick black hair and that special arrogance that makes some guys walk with their elbows out and the backs of their hands facing forward. He climbs into the front seat beside you, making no attempt to open the rear door for her.

"The liquor store, then back here."

Surprise.

"Beautiful morning," you offer.

Silence.

The first stop-light gives you a chance to glance in the rear-view mirror: she sits huddled in the far corner of the back seat—small and skinny and with that grey look that goes with too many starches and not enough hope. She's scared.

He speaks: "You ever drive transport, buddy?" The question is more a challenge than a wish to know; his voice has that phony trucker's drawl that the real pros don't bother with.

You turn to meet his hard stare. "Some. A long time ago."

"Yeah. Well, keep it that way. Too much time away from home." He looks out the window, ending the conversation.

You can take a hint. And here's the Jolly Shop.

"You comin' in with me?" he demands.

"No, Joe. I'll wait here." Her voice is as thin as she is.

He wrenches the rear door open and hauls her out by one skinny arm — if she weighed ten pounds more she'd have a dislocated shoulder—and half drags her, yelling, into the liquor store.

Sometimes it's best just to drive off and forget whatever's on the meter; even cops don't like getting into a man-and-wife scuffle. Before you can decide, they're back in the car. Still arguing. You back out of the parking space and head for their place, anxious to be rid of them before it *really* hits the fan. You find yourself doing almost sixty in a forty-mile-an-hour zone.

"You goddam bitch! How many times is this?"

"I'm sorry, Joe! I'm sorry.... You just don't know how it's been...." Her voice is a thin wail.

"Just wait till I fuckin' get you home!"

"No, Joe, please! Oh, please!"

He reaches back to cuff her with a big, meaty hand; she ducks out of his reach. Her wailing becomes a high, hysterical shriek. He leans far over the seat back and gives her a resounding crack across the face.

"Christ, am I gonna get you! And that asshole you been . . . "

Suddenly the back door opens with a blast of icy air into the car. Almost instinctively you reach back to grab the handle—and grab a handful of girl instead. She screams, hanging half out of the cab:

"Let me go! I want to die. . . . Let me go!"

Still clutching her you try to fight the car to a stop, slewing back and forth across the busy road; a glance in the mirror shows a huge gravel truck ten feet off your back bumper, air brakes hissing. The shriek of brakes almost drowns out her screams. By now most of her is being dragged along the rough pavement. A few near-misses with oncoming cars, and you finally come to a halt. You release your grip on her and she slumps to the road, bloody and still screaming. The gravel-truck driver climbs down from his cab and hurries over to help.

With that, a police cruiser stops across the road in a shower of dust and stone. The cop darts through the slowing traffic, his hand posed an inch from his gun.

The three of you pick her up and carry her to the cruiser and place her, as gently as you can, on the back seat. The cop reaches for his radio and motions you back to the car. Joe is still sitting there, staring straight ahead. He hasn't moved since the girl cracked the door open. The truck driver leans against the cab, watching the cop use the radio.

Joe reaches into his pocket, pulls out a ten-dollar bill, and places it on the seat beside you.

"What the hell is that for?"

"That's for keepin' your mouth shut. You don't know nothin'."

It's like a line from a bad movie.

"You gotta be kidding! Your wife tried to kill herself, for chrissake! Get over there and talk to her. . . . " Your voice shakes.

He sits, staring straight ahead, saying nothing. Minutes pass. The truck driver mutters something about how he nearly ran up your ass, and offers you a cigarette.

The cop finishes whatever he had to do on the radio, speaks to the girl for a minute, and ambles across to the cab. He opens the front passenger door. "This the husband?"

You nod. Joe gives you a look of pure hatred and picks up the sawbuck from the seat. "Okay, buddy." The cop takes him firmly by the arm and starts to march him across the front of the car.

"She okay?" you ask through the open window.

"Oh, she's a hell of a mess . . . lost about a yard of skin . . . but I think she'll be all right. Ambulance is on the way." The cop hustles Joe into the cruiser.

You get out of the cab and walk across the road; the cop winds his window down.

"You need me for anything?" You try to read the face under the visor of the police cap, but the eyes have gone back into uniform.

"No, nothing right now. I saw the whole thing, and that was a nice piece of driving. Go on about your business. I have your door number if I need it."

You've been dismissed. Time to get back to work.

"Seven-eight."

"Go ahead, Seven-eight."

"I been talking to the police for a while . . . in case you wondered where I was."

"Roger, Seven-eight."

Like I said, ten in the morning is no time for drama.

 THE PURSE

The old man comes through the hospital doors and hesitates, blinking in the glare of the late February afternoon.

His strong face comes through the open window of the cab: "This car for Blair?"

"Yessir. Going to Highland Creek."

He climbs into the front seat with the air of a man who is used to doing things for himself, a little embarrassed at being driven anywhere by a stranger. A big man, with the look of the railroad—or perhaps the sea—about him: weathered skin, outdoor eyes; a man who has worked hard for a lot of years, with no softness about him.

A purse, large and ornate, dangles from his big hand as if it had been attached without his notice.

Because he seems friendly you lead into the kind of neutral conversation two cordial strangers can have: hockey, inflation, the weather. His response is warm, if a trifle absent-minded.

And all the while, the purse hangs from that powerful hand.

Now, there are few things more open to bawdy comment than the sight of a man carrying a purse. Wise women know this, and it remains a rare sight. That small, silent censor in the back of your mind squashes the flippant, asinine comment before it can escape your lips.

Why bite your tongue, you wonder. Obviously his wife has sent him home with the purse to exchange it for another more suitable to her hospital stay. It happens all the time. Still, the tiny censor is stronger than your sense of the ridiculous—the conversation stays with hockey.

Suddenly, as you turn into his street, his face changes. He grips the purse as if aware, for the first time, that it is there. The beginnings of grief are in his eyes, but his voice is flat and steady. It's a terrible thing to hear.

"She died. She just died. I took her over there at noon . . . and she just died. . . . "

There isn't a thing you can say except, perhaps, "I'm sorry." You don't quite hear your own voice; maybe you said something better than that.

He indicates the driveway leading to a small, white house with a bower of willow to soften the front—a house where love may have survived forty years of marriage.

"Is there anything I can do? Anyone I can bring over? Don't worry about the fare. . . . "

"No, it's all right."

"There must be someone you want to see. . . . You shouldn't be alone."

"No. No, thanks anyway. There's no one . . ." The old man leaves the cab and stands staring at the house as if seeing it for the first time.

The purse hangs from his fingers.

The short, winter twilight begins to blur the edges of the scene, and you hope the car is utterly silent as you back out of the driveway.

It's going to be a rough night.

WHAT'S A NICE GIRL LIKE YOU...

☛ A standard myth is the one about the Whore with a Heart of Gold.

Xaviera Hollander spent a few years churning out some other myths—and the sad thing about it is that we helped her get rich in the process. I don't know whether society actually bought her little fables, but it sure as hell bought her books. Xaviera's point, of course, was that whoring is really a hell of a lot of fun—and that most of the girls in the business are lovely, intelligent, charming secretaries and sociology students putting in time until the right millionaire comes along. Just nice kids having a lot of clean, guilt-free fun. It's always such *fun*!

Bullshit. Best-selling, but still bullshit.

A splendid little bit of whimsy (I *hope* it was whimsy, because it was a classic) took place a few years ago in a paranoid little town a couple of dozen miles east of here: somebody decided to throw a civic reception and luncheon—at about $25 a plate—for Xaviera. It was a sellout; dozens of politicians and other fools were turned away at the door. A civic, standing-room-only tribute—to what? To a skinny little broad with a bad complexion and a dynamite agent.

Within a month or two she was hit with a shoplifting charge—and a deportation threat. Figure it out.

So? She found a way of making a few million—and if you like the pun, it's yours—by preaching a fantasy that a lot of people want

31

to believe, and I suppose there's nothing especially wicked about that. P. T. Barnum would've loved it.

In the taxi business you meet almost everybody, sooner or later; I've probably met a lot more hookers than I realize. There's no mark on them, no scarlet "A" on the forehead, no necessary arrogance or flamboyance. And Xaviera's right, up to a point: some of them *are* fun-loving secretaries or whatever — but not many. Most of them just look bored. In conversation (and a cab ride of three blocks can bring out some pretty astounding conversation) I find them self-centred, stupid, and lazy — almost without exception. Sometimes they'll try The Look on the cab-driver, but their hearts aren't in it. I guess they know we know.

A fun business? I'd guess that half of them have needle tracks on their arms. At least half.

☞ Trixie was a regular customer for a long time. She had a routine: a cab to go downtown at about eight in the evening (and would the driver trust her for the fare until later?) and a cab to come home at three in the morning. She was *never* broke at three in the morning, and that's when she'd peel off enough money for both fares—and a nice tip for both drivers. She never let us down, as far as I know. The routine worked just fine, every night, for two or three years.

Her base of operations was a place called Norm's Open Kitchen, right in the heart of the second-rate downtown action. I suppose the cops were sorrier than anyone when the place was finally closed down; at least they'd always known where the characters were while the joint was open.

You didn't have to look for a neon sign to find Norm's; all you had to look for was the three or four cop-cars parked out front most of the time. You could buy anything there — anything: after-hours booze, dope, porn movies, a broad, a gun—anything. I guess the cops loved the place because they knew that any bust they made there would stick; the top operators with the top shyster lawyers worked a different scene.

Norm had long since given up trying to keep plate glass in the windows, and had gone to some kind of heavy-gauge plastic sheets, which must've given the Health Department a stroke. After a lot of political horseshit (while the police commission objected as strenuously as its politically based mandate would allow), Norm was finally closed down. Since then a couple of hamburger/chicken franchises have failed spectacularly in the same spot, and the characters have moved on. So have the cops. The passing of Norm's marked the end of an era, of sorts. The nearby whorehouses are still operating, as far as I know. So much for Reform.

Anyway, Norm's is where Trixie used to ply her trade. Doing My Thing, she used to call it. "I'm going downtown to Do My Thing." She must've had a rather specialized trade: although many of the signs of what she must have been at eighteen were still there —the fine hair, the good complexion, the clear and pretty eyes—at thirty or so she weighed at least two hundred and eighty pounds. She never came home broke.

I liked her, in a way. I've often felt that there's a kind of affinity between hookers and cab-drivers on the night shift—and maybe the affinity grows from the night itself. Trixie wasn't very bright, but she was a hell of a lot better than an empty cab at three in the morning. She talked to me about her trade, but seldom in clinical terms, and with a kind of innocence that was somewhere between amusing and stupid. At least she never tried to trade for the fare.

The last time I drove her home from Norm's—a stormy midnight at least two hours before her usual quitting time—she was different. Something was bugging her. I asked her about it.

"You wanta know what I just did?" Her voice shook with rage. "I'll tell you what I just did. . . . I tried to hustle a cop. A *cop*, for chrissake!"

"Plain-clothes?"

"Well, yeah. Gimme credit for *some* brains, will ya?"

"Sorry, Trixie. That was a goddam stupid question. Sorry."

"That's okay. . . . It's no dumber than what I . . . "

"How'd it happen?"

She sighed. The car heaved on the springs, just a bit. "Well, this guy was sittin' there lookin' like a tourist . . . maybe thirty-five . . . lonely . . . "

"You mean you don't know how to spot a cop *yet?*"

"Gimme a break! This one looked like a friggin' *accountant,* for godsake. Kinda skinny . . . well, not really skinny, but not like a cop, neither. I guess it was the glasses did it . . . little gold rims."

"He bust you in Norm's?"

"Hell, no. They can't bust you for drinkin' a coffee — and I never take no money in public. No, I got this arrangement with this boarding-house up the street, and that's where he handed me my double sawbuck. . . . *Then* he busted me."

"How come he didn't haul you in?"

"Oh, they don't hardly do that no more. A lot of times they just give you a thing that looks like a traffic ticket. Here."

At the next stop I turned on the dome light and looked at the summons she'd handed me. Sure enough, it looked just like a speeding ticket. (When I get a brain transplant I'm going to insist on a unit that doesn't pop up with things like: could the cop be charged with Disturbing the Piece? I'm glad I didn't ask out loud.) I said, "Do you think he can make it stick? With no witnesses, I mean?"

She gave me a look that had none of the usual girly flutterings in it. "Are you for real? Cops don't need no witnesses, not in my business —and it ain't like this was the first time."

"What'll you get?"

"Oh, a hundred-buck fine . . . maybe thirty days suspended. They don't really want us in the can. But that's not what gripes my ass. It's my kids. . . . They told me they'd take them away from me if it happened again. That scares me."

I thought: there's always hostages, somewhere. I knew her kids; sometimes she'd phone for a cab to take the whole tribe to a McDonald's or a Saturday afternoon movie or whatever. The kids were always clean and polite—I was going to say they were just like a normal family, Mother treating the kids to a Big Mac now and then—but it wasn't quite that way, even if I *hadn't* known what Mom did for a living. Maybe the kids were *too* polite; I don't know.

I never saw Trixie again after that rainy night, but I have a hunch she had problems a little heavier than the law and the kids. A few weeks later a woman fell—somehow—from a tenth-floor balcony of the building where Trixie lived; and the tenth was Trixie's floor. At first the police figured the woman was pushed, but they never came up with any real proof. And the dead woman's name was Beatrice Something-or-other—is Trixie a diminutive for Beatrice? I think so.

The kids? It must be a rocky life for them, with or without their mother.

☞ COLLECTOR'S COLUMN

☛ Some of the guys tell me they don't run into nearly as much absurdity as I do, but I don't believe it. They're just not paying attention—or my own sense of the ridiculous has taken over (which may be the last flash of a waning sanity). Whatever. I *collect* absurdities in the way that some people collect porcelain chamber-pots.

☛ "I t'ink is just terrible!"

I turned to look in the back seat: she was probably sixty, dumpy, with the inevitable babushka thrown over her head and tied under her chin. A thick accent, maybe Polish. She was going a couple of blocks. "What's terrible, ma'am?"

"I t'ink is terrible I get different driver every time. Vy I can't get same vun always? I'm take taxi all time . . . ever' day, most."

"Do you go at the same time every morning?"

"Vhat is you say?" She leaned forward and laid a stevedore-size forearm on the seat back.

"Do you always take a taxi at seven in the morning?"

"No! No!" She waved that big arm around like a war club. "Sometime five in afternoon . . . sometime midnight. Work shift. But alvays take taxi . . ."

"But, ma'am, if you don't always go at the same time . . ." (then I wondered what the hell I was arguing about) "we can't all work night and day, you know. We have to go home some time. . . ."

She leaned back in disgust and folded her arms across her ample bosom. "Paah!" she snorted. "I still t'ink is terrible!"

☛ This one came out of the house and down the steps, staring at her feet; it's amazing how many of them stare at their feet. I opened the left rear door, the one closest to her; but, watching her feet, she didn't see it. Middle class, minked to the ears, maybe forty-five— and looking sheepish as hell.

She gave me an address downtown. After a couple of miles, I could tell she was as tense as a harp string. I said, "It's been a beautiful week, hasn't it? Hardly a cloud in the sky...."

"Oh, yes! I can hardly remember an autumn like this.... It's just gorgeous!" The tension was gone, almost as if a death sentence had been lifted from her. She chattered all the way downtown, and we had a fine time. I pulled up in front of the address she'd given me and began to write up the trip-sheet while she dug into her purse for the fare. Suddenly: "Are you writing this down?" Shocked, almost panicky.

"Sure. Why?"

"But you can't... you iust can't! Somebody might check..."

"I have to, lady. It's the law. I have to record every trip I make." I held up the clipboard for her to see.

"Why d'you have to do that?"

"Damned if I know, sometimes... I guess it's for the police, mostly. In case they have to trace somebody. All I know is I can get into a hell of a lot of trouble if I don't do it. What's the problem?"

"It's my husband..."

"Your husband? He thinks you're gonna mess around in a department store?"

"You don't understand. I've never been in a taxi before...."

"So? Most of the people in this town hardly ever take a cab."

"That's not the point. You don't know my husband."

"No, and I don't expect to." I hate this kind of twist in a

conversation; life is kinky enough without it. "What about your husband?"

"He'd *kill* me if he ever found out I took a taxi. He says all taxi drivers are thugs . . . and they rape women all the time. . . . "

"Thanks. That'll be ten-forty, please. And you can tell your husband he's wrong. Hell, I sometimes go a *whole week* without raping anyone. . . . "

Jesus Christ!

☛ I was dispatching on a quiet Sunday night.

I knew I had cars available everywhere; orders were coming in over the phone at the rate of about one every ten minutes. On a night like that, *nobody* is busy. The phone rang:

"What's the time, please?" (It'd be nice if more of 'em said "please".)

"Two-oh-nine."

"Thanks." (Maybe one in twenty says that, and the rest should damned well hang by their thumbs.)

The phone rang again: "Gimme a wake-up at six-thirty."

"Your number?"

"Three six two, seven six five one." Click. Buzz. (I'll never understand how we got sucked into stupid things like this.)

Everybody cracked back and forth over the air for a few minutes: dumb jokes, insults — the kind of stuff that keeps us sane. Then: "Answer the phone, John." (Ed had heard the phone ringing on the desk while I'd had the mike open for a few seconds.) I picked up the receiver. "Taxi."

"Is this the taxi?"

"Yes, this is the taxi. Can I help you?"

"Yeah, I'm on Westlake. How long to get a cab?"

I knew I had at least two cars at the subway station, just around the corner from Westlake. I said, "Oh, two minutes . . . maybe three."

"Fuck! That's too long!" Click. Buzz.

I often wonder if anyone else made it quicker.

☛ I buzzed the intercom at the apartment building. No answer. But it sometimes takes quite a while to come down, and maybe they were already on the way. So I waited a few minutes. Finally a woman, fiftyish, came out through the doors of the building and headed toward the car in front of me like a destroyer under forced draft. She tugged and wrestled at the door handle, but nothing gave. The other car was a Camaro or a Mustang or something.

It suddenly occurred to me that this might be my fare. (All I had was a sedan done up in flashy colours and a roof light and decals all over the place, parked about ten feet away from this woman trying to break into somebody's sports car.) I got out of the car and called to her: "Madam, this is your taxi!" When I held the door open for her, she peered at me, then sidled over to my car with the air of a woman who had been desperately insulted. I helped her into the cab and closed the door after her.

She was in full whine by the time I walked around the car and climbed behind the wheel. "I don't know why you people can't *help* a person, for heaven's sake!" (I thought I had.) "I'm going to the doctor's . . . "

There was only one answer, really. I said, "The eye doctor's, I presume."

She was not amused.

☛ The prize item in my absurdity collection is the by-law that came out of an emergency meeting of the Inspection Office a couple of years ago. These two items are separated by several paragraphs, but they read pretty much like this:

The driver must turn off *the two-way radio if the passenger requests it.* (It's the only legal weapon we have, goddammit.)

The radio may not *be turned off while the taxi is in service.*

The emergency meeting of the Office was called in the wake of a killing and a near-killing, both within a week. A cab-driver had been shot through the head; he might have been found sooner if it had been summer, but a body takes a bit longer to begin to smell when the temperature is around zero. Days later another driver had been shot in the face, but he survived. The cops cleaned that one up beautifully: they simply blew the gunman to hell.

I suppose we shouldn't complain about the ambiguity of the by-law concerning the radio; after all, they *did* decide, at that "emergency" meeting, that we should all have a medical every three years. They didn't do much about bulletproof shields between back and front seat, though.

 PAINS— THIRTY SECONDS

They say it takes longer to get an ambulance than it does to get a cab. I wouldn't know about that, but I do know that a lot of trips really *should* be ambulance runs. Maybe they call us because a taxi is a lot cheaper, but that's a little hard to believe, too; most people's health insurance pays for the ambulance.

Whatever the reason, it puts a load on the cab-driver that he's neither trained *nor paid* to handle. Maternity cases, for instance: where the hell are all the fathers hiding? If my experience means anything, about four out of five women go to the hospital *alone*; and just what, for Christ's sake, am I supposed to do with a woman who has very obviously waited a couple of hours too long before heading for the hospital? It's been a near thing more than once.

One of our louder local politicians has been pushing a scheme whereby all cab-drivers would have to take a course in midwifery. Nobody has suggested paying us a little extra, should the need for this kind of service ever arise, nor is it recorded that the same politician has ever directed his massive intellect to finding out why it takes so damned long to get an ambulance.

But I digress.

It was only about a three-mile run to the hospital, but her pains were starting to come about fifteen seconds apart. Luckily there was almost no traffic on the road, even though it was mid-afternoon. I cracked to the dispatcher: "I don't think I'll need an escort, but you'd better phone and tell them what I'm doing. I'll be

43

moving pretty good." I switched on the emergency flashers; they're better than nothing. Within seconds a cruiser passed me and swung in front, holding station about a hundred feet ahead, its red light flashing. I followed it up the hospital driveway to the Emergency doors.

She was really into it by this time: deep, breathy moans, punctuated by shrieks of pain. No man's nerves are built to stand any of that. The cop helped me carry her to the Emergency doors, where we were met by an intern and two nurses with a wheeled stretcher. I cursed the idiot guard who hadn't bothered to wheel out one of the dozen wheel-chairs lined up inside the doors. I'm not crazy about hospitals, so I stayed by the car while the cop disappeared inside. Within a minute he came back with a roll of paper towels. "Looks like her water broke in your car," he said.

The birth process—the ultimate miracle—doesn't concern itself with situational aesthetics; if we think it's a messy business, that's *our* problem. A miracle doesn't have to be neat. But the cop was right, and my next fare wouldn't have been interested in any explanations for the state of the back seat and floor. The cop and I spent at least fifteen minutes cleaning it up, and we finally borrowed a disinfectant spray from the hospital.

Then we leaned against the car, smoking, talking about baseball, watching the lamb-shaped clouds drift across the sky. It was a rare moment, in a way: a cop and a civilian sharing a small corner of a mystery. I wondered how it was going with her in there, and whether she was bearing the son she wanted. (She'd been able to tell me that much, between the pains.) Finally I flicked my cigarette away, tossed a small salute at the cop, and moved toward the driver's door of my car.

"Hold it a minute, buddy."

I've long since learned to recognize that special cop tone of voice. I said, "Yeah? Is there something else?"

"Sure is." He reached into the cruiser and brought out his summons book. I couldn't believe it.

"You givin' me a ticket? For what?"

"Speeding. Two red lights. Improper use of emergency flashers."

"Come *on*, officer... you helped me carry her in there, for chrissake! You've gotta be joking...."

"No joke, buddy. Tell you what... I'll drop the bit about the emergency flashers."

There's no sane way to argue with a cop. And if you're big enough to get physical about it, you just lose that much harder. I'm not big enough, but I was steaming: "That is the dirtiest, cheapest, most miserable shot I ever heard of in my whole goddam life!"

"So? You'll get a chance to tell that to the judge. Here." He ripped the ticket from his book and handed it to me. (The bit about the flashers *was* there, by the way.)

Months later, I got my chance to tell it to the judge. He wanted to go along with the cop, but I'd brought along the order ticket, dated and time-stamped by machine. It's just about impossible to fake them; and scrawled across the bottom of the ticket, clearly in the same order-taker's handwriting as the rest of the order, were the words: "pains 30 sec."

I beat that one, but I think it would be best if I never ran into that cop again. Hell, I never even collected the two-eighty for my fare. After all that bullshit.

☞ THE NIGHT THE GREEK SMILED

☞ I guess it's true that money talks; but you don't often hear it laugh. And if the Greeks had a word for just about everything, they probably didn't have one to describe what happens when certain facial muscles contract — unless they just lumped it right in there with the word for "indecent exposure".

Not among your really great smilers, the Greeks.

Maybe it's a religious thing: I imagine this secret shrine, hidden away in the boonies a hundred miles from Athens. The place is kept secret from everyone — except those who are about to emigrate to this country. Those people *have* to visit the shrine; it's part of the deal in getting a visa. And in this holy place there is preserved a scrap of ancient parchment, a sacred writ, declaring:

Go Ye Now And Establish A Restaurant. And Let Not The Barbarian Tempt Thee Into Levity With Cunning Merriment And Daily Spending Of Much Gold Within Thy Place. For In Levity Lieth Damnation. And Much Reduction Of The Profit.

Perhaps I exaggerate. But think about it, anyway.

☞ They're really pretty good guys, all four of them; it just takes a while to get to know them. Thirty years might do it.

They run a nice place, and I suppose Jim's the boss; at least he does most of the visible worrying. I wouldn't want to ask who owns how much of what; the question would be greeted with some hostility, I think. Maybe all four brothers have equal shares, but we'll never know.

Nick is next in line. Being the *second* brother in a Greek family must take a lot of the heat off; Nick is almost relaxed, most of the time.

George, number three, seems preoccupied lately: it must be his new responsibility, I suppose. He went home for a month's holiday a couple of years ago and came back — half a year later — with a new bride. I think Jim would've shot him if he'd come back alone, especially after abandoning the family business for so long. The only way to get a rise out of George these days is to ask about the baby; the corners of his mouth almost lift when he talks about his son.

Spiro isn't around the place enough to understand the gravity of the situation. One of these days — a careless moment, an instant's lapse — and all of that young man's training is going to go down the chute. Levity lurks very close to the surface in Spiro.

And Papa. What can I say about the wonderful, tough, old sonofabitch with the gleam in his eye — just like he'd invented it? The waitresses walk in wide circles past him, unless they're too tired to worry about a random pinch on the ass, or whatever. There was the time Liz got into some kind of argument about whether or not her boobs were real. Papa settled that. (They are.)

The Suburban is where most of us grab breakfast or lunch, or — depending on the shift we work — a beer and a sandwich when things begin to slow down around midnight. You'll seldom drive past the place without seeing at least one cab parked in front. I suppose you'd call it a hangout for cab-drivers, but Jim would never let it become the kind of place "hangout" might suggest to a lot of people. (Hell, salesmen are a whole lot louder and they stay longer; but you've never heard of a hangout for salesmen.)

There's a good trade from the hospital on the next corner: technicians and office staff — nurses don't spend money — but I've never heard it said that the hospital enjoys a return trade from the

Suburban. The food ranges from better-than-average to pretty damned good. Nick excels himself a couple of times a week and turns out a Special that is very close to superb. At about half the downtown price.

Of course, none of this explains why we've made the place a kind of headquarters for conversation over a drink or two. (The serious drinkers go to a place called the Cameo, but that's another story.) Why the Suburban for most of us? Well, it can't be because Jim jumps for joy whenever one of the bunch walks in; but it might be because we all know that Jim, like most cab-drivers, has seen just about everything; we have that in common—an unspoken kinship, in a way. It may also be because he refuses to hire a rock group, to make the place look busier, and that keeps out the kiddie trade. You can talk.

Yeah, Jim sees it all: the beginnings and ends of feuds and friendships; quiet discussions over two or three drafts, noisy arguments over a dozen; and romance (if the word still means anything). More than a few of us have met HER there.

And through it all, Jim wouldn't change expression if you lit a bomb under his ass.

☛ One night the gang of us were sitting at the back, near the TV—a football game, I think it was—so we didn't hear the scuffle starting by the cash register. Jessie let out a little yelp as she placed a tray of drinks on the table. I turned just in time to see Jim hustling a couple of young punks out the front door.

We've learned not to worry too much about Jim in these situations. (Like his brothers he has big forearms, *really* big forearms— and a low centre of gravity; any one of the four could take on an ox —and the ox would be on the menu the next day.) But a few of the guys got up and started toward the front anyway. Suddenly there was one hell of a crash and the chiming of falling glass—and the whole front window was gone. A car roared in the parking lot, then we heard the shriek of tires laying a lot of rubber.

After a few seconds Jim came back in, paused to examine something he took from the cash drawer, and stolidly began dialling the phone.

By this time a half-dozen of us were up at the front, examining the gaping window and stepping around the big shards of glass strewn on the floor. One of the heavy litter-cans from outside, about the size and weight of an oil drum, lay in the middle of the mess.

"Hokay," Jim said after a minute's conversation on the phone, and hung up. He rang No Sale on the cash register and put something in the drawer.

"P'leece comin' now," he said. He looked about as ruffled as if he'd been counting the cash.

We know better than to press him for details; he'll tell you what he wants you to know — if anything — in his own damned good time. We wandered back to the table and Jessie brought another round.

The cops were there within five minutes. I couldn't hear the discussion, but I could see Jim take a piece of paper about the size of a dollar bill from the register and show it to them. One of the cops took notes, then they left. Jim came back to our table.

"Jessie," he said, "see what ev'body's want. I'm buy." He leaned against the next table and waited for us to ask what the hell had happened. We obliged.

"Those craz' bastard," he said after we'd finished shouting questions, "they all finish drink and Liz give 'em bill and they pay..."

"They paid?" someone asked.

"Oh, sure! They pay. Then start give Liz bad time. I don' like my girls get bad time from punks. Then they mouthy with me on way out."

"Is Liz okay?" (We all like Liz and Jessie.)

"Sure. But maybe I let her off bit early, one you guys drive her home. I pay."

I looked over to where Liz was clearing a table. She looked more furious than upset.

"Anyway," Jim went on, "they mouthy with me, I say 'No more, don' come back here!' One guy he's want fight so I put 'em out. Then he's throw can through window and they bot' fuck off in car."

"You get the licence number?"

Then Jim laid it on us: a big, slow, wide smile. Every tooth showed; the corners of his eyes crinkled.

It was one hell of a shock.

"Licence numb'?" he asked. He waved the piece of paper he'd shown the cops. "Don' need! Those craz' punks, know what they do? Those stupid sonabitch pay by Chargex!"

☞ NOTHING EXCEEDS LIKE EXCESS

☛ It is written somewhere: society is based upon what men *think* themselves to be, rather than upon what they really are.

I don't know about that; it sounds a bit too simple to me. I know several horses' asses who *think* they're something else entirely, but they're still horses' asses. Consider, for example, the factory sweeper who wears a suit and tie to ride the bus to work (carrying his lunch in an attaché case) and changes to overalls in the plant washroom; or, worse, the cab-driver who carries an attaché case with *nothing* in it. As if society gave a damn.

All of which is a roundabout way of getting to Doug: he decided to think of himself as a degenerate, a bum, a total loss. Society may not have given a damn, but *we* did. He never fell into the hands of those statistical fascists called social workers, not quite, but it was a near thing. I think that would've finished Doug for good.

I'm damned if I'll ever understand what drives some guys — totally aware of what's happening to them — straight into the deepest, shittiest part of the gutter. "Alcoholism!" the social worker will shout. "Death-wish," the psychiatrist may mutter, after an interval devised to hide the fact that he hasn't the slightest goddam idea why a man will suddenly decide to roll in filth.

(I can understand inadvertence and bad luck and inferior body chemistry and all the other things that sometimes combine to nudge a man into a swamp of booze and despair; it's the willing *dive* into the gutter that confounds me.) Hell, I see a dozen hopeless cases every day—so do most cab-drivers—and Doug must certainly have seen his share.

☞ It all started quite suddenly:

"I think my wife's leaving me. Finally." Doug took a tentative sip of the steaming coffee on the counter in front of him.

I hadn't known this side of him, even though we'd driven opposite shifts on the car for a couple of months. "I didn't know you had that kind of problem. . . ."

"Problem? What problem? We've been at each other's throats for two or three years . . . ever since I went bankrupt. I'm just glad she decided to give up buggin' me."

"You went bankrupt? From what?"

"From the construction business. I thought you knew. I used to build roads, bridges, stuff like that. Hell, I used to have over thirty trucks and 'dozers . . ."

"What happened?" I glanced at the clock on the wall of the donut joint: four-fifteen a.m. Time for Doug to get to work, and time for me to go home. It had been a long night.

"The goddam government, that's what happened. I had to pay *my* bills in thirty days, and meet a payroll every week. But the sons of bitches took about half a year to pay *me*. And back in '70 the banks weren't lendin' a bloody dime. . . ."

"So you went under."

"Went under? Shit, I made a splash like the waves are *still* lappin' the shore! If I gave a damn, I could spend the next ten years in court."

"You don't give a damn?"

"For what? The equipment, the house, the pool, the cars . . . the whole goddam thing is long gone . . . and the bastards'd garnishee me right now, if they could."

"Really?"

"Sure. Why the hell do you think I'm in the cab business? They can't touch me!"

(It's true. This country is one of the last places in the civilized world where a garnishee of wages is still possible in law. But cab-drivers, being legally self-employed, are exempt. Since most employers are terrified of garnishees against their workers, the welfare rolls are full of people who will never work again — until they pay off a debt with money they'll never have. The system is self-defeating, to say the least.)

I said, "You mean your wife is going to leave you because you're driving a cab?"

"*That's* a dumb question. You're not listening. I blew a fortune, remember?"

"So . . . ?"

"So every woman would like to believe she's entitled to marry into success. Most of 'em are smart enough to know it isn't really gonna happen, but give one of 'em a taste of it . . . and then blow it . . . and look out!"

"You got kids, Doug?"

"Yeah, a girl . . . she'll go with her mother, I guess . . . and a boy. But he'll be leavin' home any day now. I just want to get the whole damned thing over with, that's all."

"What'll you do when your wife's gone . . . if she really goes?"

Doug snorted. "Hah! I'll do me some *real* drinkin' and screwin' and fightin', that's what I'll do!"

☛ The address became a real pain in the ass after a while:

"Seven-eight, it's your buddy again."

"Don't tell me. Twenty-seven-oh-three. Apartment two-ten."

"Right on! How'd you figure that out?"

"Just lucky, I guess. What's he want now?"

Depending on the time of night, the order could be for anything from smokes, to a bottle, to taking one of Doug's women home to the other end of the city — and Doug would pay tomorrow. Tomorrow never seemed to come, but that's not what bothered me.

Doug was pushing forty, but he liked his stuff young; the oldest looked about eighteen. I'm trying to think of a word that would describe most of them; "slut" and "baby whore" and "cheap little bitch" come to mind, but they all lack sufficient force and scope. A sweep of third-rate cat-houses would've turned up a better class of broads. It's not that they were all ugly — some of them were far from that — but most of them looked as if they'd learned to paint their faces without ever learning to wash them; I sometimes felt I should scrub out the back seat after one of them left the car. (It wasn't always just *one* that I drove home; it was often two or three. I've wanted to be invited to an orgy for a long time, but I think I'd pass on one of Doug's.)

The language on some of those long, dark trips was enough to make a Suez stevedore cringe.

It went on like that for months: a constant stream of booze and broads in and out of Doug's apartment, night after night after night. I don't know how the hell his body stood it, but he was always ready to go at four-fifteen in the morning, when I picked him up to start his shift. But his women never seemed to have a nickel, and I was by no means the only one who'd had to take one of them twenty or thirty miles on a promise.

We all got pretty goddam sick of it.

☛ There's something wrong with the ending of this story. The forces of Righteousness did *not* drive Doug into the waiting arms of the Welfare Machine; he was never given a number—and he never knew the warmth and reassurance of the monthly visit with his Social Worker.

Something snapped. He got rid of the child sluts and quit phoning to see if any of his buddies would pick up a bottle for him. It didn't happen overnight: I'd say the process took close to a year— which means about five hundred bottles of booze delivered by cab, and at least a hundred of those strange, grubby little girls. (I *still*

can't figure out where he found them. Is there an agency somewhere?)

Anyway, Doug quit driving cab. The last I heard, he had three
trucks on the road. I see him occasionally; he still needs a cab home
from the Knobby once in a while, but he's on the way back.
Definitely. Rumour has it that he's lucked onto a nice, sane little
chick who knows how to wash her face.

I hope it works out.

THE WORD OF A LADY

■ The detection and apprehension of criminals works pretty well in this town; we have one of the best police forces anywhere—and one of the worst courts systems. Maybe the courts are jammed because the cops are *too* good at their job; somebody figured out that the average criminal conviction takes about thirty seconds. A judge under that kind of pressure isn't likely to come out of it looking like the very embodiment of Justice, and it means that some pretty heavy action receives sentences that are about as rough as having your library card lifted.

Someone observed that Justice is about Truth—and Law is about Lying. Take a look around any courtroom: check out the tailoring of some of the lawyers—and tell me how much chance Truth really has. But, dammit, you've got to have a lawyer; nobody else could possibly figure out the rules. Get one who has lunch with the judge once in a while.

Pete didn't want a lawyer. "They told me I don't need one."

"*Who* told you?" Pete was letting them lead him right into a trap. "What's the charge, exactly?"

"Something about 'failure to be civil . . .' "

Good Jesus! They were going to hang him for being rude! Pete is one of the good guys; rudeness isn't something you'd notice about him. He's big as statues, good-looking—and black. If he's defensive about his colour, I don't know anyone who's ever seen him show it. His wife is a stunning blonde; I'd say Pete is pretty comfortable about who he is.

"Hell, Pete, I can get all the guys to chip in . . . we'll *buy* you a lawyer."

"Nope. They told me bringing a lawyer to the hearing would only make the whole thing look more serious than it really is. I should stay cool, like it's nothing important."

"Bullshit! Don't you know who you're up against?"

"Sure. The Office. They sent a guy around to see me . . . he seemed like a nice guy . . . and he said the worst thing I can do is over-react. It's nothin' to worry about."

The Office. The Inspection Office; even Kafka wouldn't believe it. If we had a Bill of Rights that really worked, the Office would be out of business in ten seconds. It licenses and regulates everything from hairdressers to butcher shops, but it saves most of its heavy action for the taxi business; and it doesn't like drivers, much. I trust the Office about as far as I could heave a locomotive.

Your plumber may be arrogant, your barber may be surly, your butcher may become downright insulting. Try to charge them with being "uncivil" and see how far you get. But Pete had been rapped with "failure to be civil . . ." (whatever in hell *that* means), and it was going to hit the fan in large loads.

"Pete, what's the date of the hearing? We're gettin' you a lawyer . . ."

"How many times've I gotta tell you? I don't *want* one!"

He wouldn't tell me when the hearing was coming up, but he did tell me the story:

Morning rush-hour. His fare was a woman, well dressed, looking like class. She was going downtown from one of the better suburbs — and she was one of those "turn here, turn there" types that make most drivers want to climb the venetian blinds.

"Exactly where are we going, ma'am?"

"I'll tell you where to turn."

"Yes, ma'am, but maybe I can miss the worst of the traffic if you'll just . . . "

"I said I'd *tell* you where to turn."

"Of course, but if you'll tell me the address . . . downtown is a big place."

"Fuck you, nigger!"

Pete says he pulled over to the side of the road at that point. "Madam, it's obvious you'd be happier in another cab, and I'll try to get you one. Meanwhile, this is as far as I care to take you."

"The hell with you, you black bastard! You'll goddam well take me where I'm going!"

"Or what, ma'am?"

"Or I'll have your hide, you bloody ape!"

Pete used the radio (I heard him) trying to find another cab clear in the area; but he couldn't. It was one of those freak mornings when the whole town has to have a taxi, instantly. I think I would've left her standing there, but I guess Pete has learned the kind of forbearance that most of us will never have to worry about. He swallowed his pride and took the woman the rest of the way. He says she even tipped him fifty cents at the end of the trip.

Late that afternoon he had a visit from the Office. His fare had laid a charge. It's just crazy enough to make sense.

I believe Pete's story because I know him; and I know how some fares can twist the truth. And of course the Office doesn't mind hanging a driver when it can. Some complaints are valid, of course: we have our share of bums and surly types—but Pete just isn't one of them.

(I often think, if truckers and neurosurgeons and archbishops had to relate to the public all day, every day, it would soon be evident that no one profession has a corner on the surliness market. How often does a drill-press operator have to be polite?)

Pete had about five seconds to tell his story in court.

The judge said: "I don't need to hear any more. It's the word of a lady against that of a cab-driver, and I'm prepared to take the lady's word. Sixty dollars and costs.'' He banged his gavel and the hearing was over. At these hearings there's no appeal—at least I've never heard of an appeal. Pete says the whole thing took about a minute.

He paid the fine, tore up his cabbie's licence and scattered the pieces all over the judge's desk. He was almost charged with contempt — which, on thinking about it, probably understated Pete's feelings by a wide margin.

The lady *did* have a lawyer, by the way. It seems odd: why spend a hundred dollars or more, just to prove a rudeness charge? It hardly seems worth while. Pete is convinced that her lawyer was hired by the Office.

Could be. I know those bastards.

The hell of it is, Pete is a better man than most of the people in this idiot business—drivers, owners, inspectors, tame judges—but he's gone, and he'll never be back. He's exactly the kind of man the business needs.

 # THE LOSERS

☛ Maybe I wasn't really listening, but I caught something about her being an ex-cop or a prison matron, something like that, and there sure wasn't much reason to doubt her.

She was a *big* woman, in height as well as in at least two other ways. The two other ways were aimed at my back like a couple of armoured gun-turrets. There's an upper limit to reasonable mammary development, at which point the goodies cease to be enticing and become, instead, objects of awe and the cause of consternation wherever they go. Nobody knows where the hell to look. If you could ignore those two stupendous distractions, she really wasn't a bad-looking woman: fortyish and probably late-blooming.

If she was an ex-cop, we were a s.w.a.t. team of two; the tactical problem was to find her husband, or at least his car. It was Saturday night, and she was positive he'd be at his new girlfriend's place. (I wondered what she'd do if she *did* find him—and hoped to hell I wouldn't have to stick around to watch.) The air rang with her stern instructions until we found ourselves on a road called Dingwall Street. And yes, Virginia, there really *is* such a street. There's a Sesame Street too.

Dingwall is a couple of blocks long, and easily wide enough for two bicycles and a small donkey-cart; and parking is permitted, which adds an interesting touch. I guess it took me ten minutes to drive those two blocks, looking for her husband's red Camaro. There's no way you can miss a red Camaro; it wasn't there. Getting back out to the main street involved some of the narrowest driving I've ever done in my life.

"Okay, love. So he's not here. Let's go to the Beach."

After a flash of mild panic I realized she wasn't looking for a blanket party; she wanted to look for the car in that deep-shaded neighbourhood of pure Canadian Gothic known as The Beach — where the natives think of the rest of the city as the dark side of another planet.

"Yeah, I guess the sonofabitch has gone back to Julie. Goddam that little whore, anyway. Okay . . . three-oh-seven Pine Crescent."

I knew the street: cool and stately and gorgeous. A road paved in red brick and winding through some of the best geography in town; a lot of the original money had long since moved on, but the switch to flats and other discreet ways of helping to pay the mortgage was not yet visible.

We tried the street, the back lanes; I even explored a couple of dark driveways on foot. A few very large dogs were not pleased to meet me. I climbed back into the car and said, "Sorry, dear. Another blank . . . just like last week and the week before. Why don't you give it up?"

"No damned way! That bastard is out whoring around somewhere, and I'm gonna find him!" She gave me a couple more addresses; with the same result. No red Camaro anywhere. She slumped in the back seat, beaten. Even those awesome boobs looked less threatening, as if her bra straps had admitted defeat, too.

Finally: "Home?"

"Yeah, sure. He must've found another one I don't know about yet. Yeah, take me home, love. You want a beer when we get there? I could stand some company . . ." Her voice was suddenly young — and very wistful.

"Aw, dammit, dear . . . you know how it is on a Saturday night. It's the weekends that pay the rent in this business. I gotta hang in here for hours, yet. Another time maybe. Okay?"

"Sure, love. Sure. Another time." She sighed, lit a cigarette, and settled back in the seat. The silence got pretty thick. The meter read seventeen dollars when we wheeled into her driveway; she dropped a twenty on the front seat and waved off my attempt to dig for change. "Prob'ly see you next week, love." She hesitated a moment, then said, "Y'know . . . that big dumb slob could get all he needs at home, with no hassle . . . no hassle at all. And he wouldn't have to hide from nobody."

She climbed out of the car and gave me a small wave and a rueful smile. Then, apparently recognizing a couple of her neighbours, she straightened her shoulders and marched toward the doors of the apartment building like a one-woman parade.

I watched her fish for her key and had a bizarre thought: it occurred to me — entirely without the slightest hint of evidence — that there *is* no husband, and there never was.

Ridiculous? Of course. So prove I'm wrong.

☛ I try to keep out of these things; I really do try.

This one came out of the tavern and immediately began to lay her life story on me. At this point my hearing usually becomes rather selective; I listen for the appropriate moments to say "Yes" or "No" or "Really?" or "Shit!" I guess I hear the whole story, but it gets a bit hard to react properly after a while. Especially when they're in that nearly-whaled state that makes a woman just slightly less dangerous than a school of barracuda.

We were going to his mistress's place, and she was going to have a quiet talk with both of them. She still loved him and wanted him back — and the kids; what about the kids, for chrissake — even though he *was* a rotten bastard. But she'd talk to him, and maybe he'd come home where he belonged. He *had* to come home.

I wasn't too crazy about the address when we pulled up in front of the place: a probably-crummy apartment over a definitely-crummy store on the Danforth. I said, "You goin' to stay a while? Or do you want me to wait?"

"Wait, please. Yeah, you better wait. Okay?"

"Okay. But I gotta leave the meter running . . ."

"Tha's all right. I won't be long."

I waited for her to get out of the car — thinking that every psychiatrist should drive hack for a month out of every year—but she didn't move. I said, "Look, dear, this is costing you." I pointed to the meter, still ticking. "Maybe I better just leave you here... you can always get another cab back when you're ready...."

"No! No, you can't leave me!"

"Well, okay. But are you going up there, or what?" (A meter ticking away on "Waiting Time" isn't all that thrilling; for the driver, it works out to slightly less than the minimum legal wage.)

"I can't go up there... I just can't. Would you..."

"Would I what?"

"Would you go up there and tell him I'm waiting? It's apartment 'A'."

"Now come *on*, dear! You don't want a cab-driver, you want a kamikaze pilot!"

"What's that?"

"Never mind. I am *not* going up there to rescue your husband from his girlfriend, and that's *it*!"

"But I can't... I have to see him... and the kids..." She broke up all over the place. I began to feel like a turd. Blubbering women do nothing for your powers of concentration, a fact of which they are damned well aware, I'm sure.

I said, "Okay, dear. You win. I'll try to get him down here to the car, but I know I'm asking for trouble."

"It'll be all right, really. He's really a very gentle guy."

The cab-driver's Heaven is a place where the people in the back seat solve their own damned problems; a place where you just do what you're supposed to do: drive them from point A to point B and collect your legal tariff without comment. A place where logic works, at least most of the time. It bears no resemblance to the real world.

I climbed those damned stairs and hammered on the door of apartment "A". There was a cooked-cabbage smell that must have hung about the place for at least a year. The air was exhausted. I could hear scurryings in the apartment and the *clink!* of glasses being cleared from the coffee table. I heard a female voice say, quite clearly through the door, "Now who the fuck would *that* be at this time of night?" There were more sounds, the sounds of habitual argument, then the door flew open.

"Yeah?" His shoulders were approximately the width of a bulldozer blade and he must have bumped his head a lot—on the tops of doorframes. Of the several impressions he made, glaring down at me, gentle was not one of them. "What the hell ya want? *What?*" It wasn't a question: it was a declaration of war.

"Well, I, ah... your wife's down in the car..."

"My wife? My *wife*? I ain't seen that dumb bitch in months. What the Christ does *she* want... and who in shit are *you*?"

"I brought her here in the cab. She's down front... she wants to talk to you..."

"Piss on that! Here, you can give her a message."

I remember thinking: Good! No time to duck; ducking would only make this idiot madder...

He must've pulled the punch a bit—my face wasn't totalled, as I found out later. But I bleed beautifully. There seemed to be no point in continuing the interview, so I went back down to the car to deliver the message.

She was gone. The meter read eight-twenty.

Some day I'll learn. (I keep saying that.) Incidentally, a really decent nose-bleed can last for over two hours, in case you were wondering.

☛ The phone booth was there all right, but where the hell was my fare? I'd only been about a block away when the order came over the radio. They can't disappear in fifteen seconds. I looked across the road to the brightly lit Traveler—we get a few motel calls at this time of night—but there was nobody in sight.

She must've been standing in the shadows behind the phone booth, checking me out for a few seconds. At two in the morning, why shouldn't she? She came toward the car, hesitating, then opened the back door and climbed in. (You can tell the people who almost never need to take a cab; she was one of them.) I didn't get much of a look at her, except to gain the impression that she was expensively dressed, and somewhere in her late thirties. She gave me an address that went with the clothes—but was curiously out of phase with that crummy motel. (Phoning from across the street wouldn't fool a ten-year-old.)

She started to cry: a genteel, Branksome Hall–type weeping at first; then great, wracking sobs that seemed to be ripping her apart. Like most men, I'm totally intimidated by a woman's tears—even though I know that with some women they can mean anything from crushing despair to mild disappointment. I'd bet that the sounds coming from the back seat, this time, had nothing to do with mild disappointment.

It was a half-hour ride. I stopped in the driveway of a house shaded by trees that were leafy and full a hundred years ago; the street was as old and as awesome as the money that had built it. I waited until she'd disappeared through the front door of the house before I backed into the street.

Two in the morning, a sleazy motel, a class chick going back to where she belonged — and crying her eyes out. I guess life isn't simple for anybody.

☞ MY OLD MAN WOULD'VE KILLED ME

☞ I'm often asked: "Who are your best customers? Who takes cabs the most?"

There's no one answer: it depends on the time of day, the day of the week, the way the driver likes to work. A night-shift driver who likes playing the streets will probably find that most of his fares are drunks; a day-shift driver with a really professional approach—and a damned good memory — may find that a good chunk of his income derives from running parcels around town. It's a lucrative corner of the business, but it requires skills I never really developed. A driver with a good parcel trade can do very well indeed.

For the rest of us, it usually goes something like this:

Early, early morning is airport time; with any luck at all — and provided he's out by 4:00 or 5:00 — a driver can grab an airport shot, and the fifteen- to eighteen-dollar fare (plus tip) is a nice leg up on the rest of the day. The airport trade is all over by about 7:00. Then come the nurses going to work. (They *never* tip. I think nurses are fantastic, and I admire the hell out of what they do for humanity — but I'm still waiting to see one of them spend some money. On *anything*.)

Now it's time for the people who've overslept and can't take a chance on public transit. Generally, these are the ones who can't quite understand why a cab doesn't materialize at their door roughly thirty seconds after they phone, if not sooner. Naturally, this part of the business is a bit "iffy". It can be dynamite one

69

morning, and nonexistent the next; it's a part of the trade that's a little hard to take seriously.

There will probably be a lull between 8:30 and 10:00, when the overweight women start tripping to the doctor's. The doctor trade is pretty steady until about 3:00 — and if you can't get your medical degree in three days, you're just not listening — then it's change-over time, when the day drivers start to head for the car-wash and the garage. Most night drivers are on the road by 4:30.

Now the tempo changes, and the pattern is gone. Apart from a few parcel runs that may go between 4:00 and 5:00, the rest of the night shift will depend entirely on public whim: people are either going out on the town — or they're not. It averages out, though: most of the longer runs go in the evening, and ten-dollar fares are not at all unusual.

The pattern returns at about 11:00, when the girls start to go home from Bingo. It's a flurry that can be worth eight or ten dollars, as long as you don't mind little old broads fighting over you — and don't ever think that Bingo-players don't fight over cabs. And they lie a lot, if you ask whether they phoned. But it's something to do on a quiet night.

Later, the taverns close. A profitable half-hour — as long as you don't mind what crawls through the back of your car.

So, the drunks are finally home from the taverns. Now it's *really* quiet. Who else is left? The air can go almost completely dead for a couple of hours — until our next little rush-hour starts.

And who might this be, you ask?

It's fifteen-year-olds, going home from their girlfriends' (or boyfriends') places. At 3:00 a.m. The same time, night after night, week after week. I don't know where the hell they get the money; it's always the same ones.

This probably makes me a dinosaur, but I know one thing for damned sure: even if *her* old man would've let me hang around that late every night (which is preposterous) — *my* old man would've killed me.

So, to get back to the original question: who are our *best* customers? There's no answer, not really. Our most *consistent* customers are children. Figure it out.

Like I said, my old man would've killed me.

☞ THE SHOT-GLASS JUNGLE

☞ When it takes two waitresses and the manager to pour your fare into the car, you know it isn't going to be the happiest of relationships during the next few minutes. And this one was a classic.

I guess the thing I *really* resent about hauling drunks is not the drunks themselves—it's the bartenders and tavern owners who'll keep serving some poor idiot as long as he can still reach for his wallet. After that, a simple phone call makes it *my* problem. It makes me feel like a kind of garbage-disposal service. And believe this: there are lots of tavern owners who, after satisfying themselves that the customer's wallet doesn't contain a nickel, will *still* call a cab to get rid of him. It isn't easy to come out even in a situation like that.

But, to get back to my classic. A smaller, skinnier, more sodden mess of humanity would be hard to imagine. It must've taken five minutes to steer him through the doors of the tavern and into my car. (The most rudimentary flash of intelligence would've made me just drive off and leave the whole preposterous scene to work itself out some other way—probably at the expense of another driver—but I didn't do that; I let them load this stunned, slobbering asshole into the back seat.)

I said, "Where to, friend?" I might as well have asked him the value of *pi* to a hundred decimal places. He was not tracking, to put it mildly. I tried again. "Where're we going, chief?"

The results were a little better this time: "Whazza framill. (Urp!) Fornagazz warmerfarggh!"

Sure. I stopped the car at the edge of the big parking-lot, right where it exits onto the east-west highway. And wondered, for the thousandth time, how the hell I manage to get into these things. "Okay, buddy!" I tried to sound firm, like a grade-three arithmetic teacher. "Which way do we go? East or west?"

"Eesh! Eesh!"

East. Fair enough. I hung a right into the highway traffic while he mumbled something that almost made sense; I was sure I caught the word "motel" in there somewhere. It helped. The motel strip was a few miles east of us, which at least cut the possible destinations down to about fifty. I soon found that we'd reached a plateau in our negotiations, though: he became lucid just long enough to tell me that he couldn't remember *which* motel—but he'd know it when he saw it. Hah! In his condition this little creep wouldn't have known his own mother if he'd tripped over her. I said, "How about your key? You must have a motel key with the name-tag on it. . . ."

"Hey, yeah! Tha's right!"

"You want to show it to me?" Silence. I waited for a few seconds, working my way through the weekend traffic, figuring he was probably going through his pockets for the key. At the first stop-light I turned to look at him: he'd passed out on me. I let out a roar: "The key! Where's the goddam key?"

It's funny, the way some skills never quite leave you. I suspect that even my own kids don't believe it, but I *did* do a bit of time as a drill-sergeant; it seems a hundred years ago, but I guess some of the parade-square bellow is still there when I need it. (They used to tell me I could be heard two miles away—when the wind was in the right direction. Hell, maybe so. I don't really remember that part of myself.) Whatever. That skinny little fart in the back seat damned near jumped out of his skin; for two or three seconds, he was probably as close to sober as he'd been in a month. "The key?

Sure, sure! It's right here some place. Jussa minute . . ."

I waited. Again. And, again, he'd passed out on me. But, as if to show me that those few seconds of sobriety had taken everything he had, he absolutely refused to wake up again; even a couple of open-handed swipes across his face accomplished nothing. He snorted and grunted like a rooting hog, but that was all. Well, hell. Over the years I've discovered damned few good reasons for going through a man's pockets, but this seemed like one of them. I stopped the car and turned on the dome light. I tried every pocket but the one in which I could feel his wallet—I will *not* go through a guy's wallet — and there was nothing resembling a motel-room key. Shit, this little clown was so hammered that he could've been thinking of a motel he'd lived in ten years ago. And searching a wallet is a cop's job.

I had a good hunch there'd be a radar car just over the next rise; it had been one of their favourite speed-traps for years—and a cop is a cop is a cop. And sure enough, there they were: two of them, in a brown Plymouth Fury that shouldn't fool anyone who drives more than a thousand miles a year.

I made a point of coming up to the cruiser at a good ten miles under the speed limit and pulled over to the side of the road, two or three car-lengths ahead. I know it's cool to think of the fuzz as being maybe a little short in the smarts department, but that's not the way things *really* are. Not by a damned sight, they aren't. There may be cops who lack imagination, and there are certainly plenty of them for whom the job is an ego trip. I've known cops I wouldn't mind having as friends, and I've known cops I wouldn't piss on if their asses were on fire. But I've never met one who was anywhere near stupid. And, what the hell? There's always that time of night when there seems to be nothing on the road but cabs and cop cars, when the only customers in the all-night donut shops are drivers and cops, and when—it'll happen, sure as hell, if you stay in the business long enough—you need, you really *need*, a cop to help you keep that precious, unique butt of yours in one piece. So we develop a mutual understanding that has nothing to do with whether or not we like each other.

I watched these two in the rear-view as they climbed out of the brown Plymouth, casual as hell and as alert as snakes. They knew I hadn't been speeding, and they knew I knew it. The younger one came up to my side of the car and motioned for me to roll down my window. "May I see your driver's licence, sir?" I got out of the car, reaching for my wallet, and noticed the other cop coming up to the rear door on the other side. His hand wasn't more than an inch from his gun. I had no chance to tell him it wasn't quite *that* kind of problem. The young one, pretending to study my licence, led me back toward the cruiser—but his eyes never really left his partner.

"You want to tell me what the hell this is all about?"

"Sure. Just a drunk. He keeps passing out on me, and I can't find out where the fuck he lives. He said something about a motel, but there's no key on him. And I hate like hell going through his wallet for I.D. I was hopin' you guys'd do it for me. I got to find an address of some kind, or I'll be stuck with this slob for the rest of the night."

"Yeah, I know what you mean. Okay, we'll check him out." We walked back toward my car. Meanwhile, the other cop had opened the passenger door, and my fare was engaged in lively conversation with him. The older cop was saying, "All we want is your address, so the driver can take you home. You *do* want to go home, don't you? Do you have a driver's licence or something?"

"Oh, sure! Sure, officer. Jussa second . . . here it is!"

The cop passed the licence over to me: if the address meant anything, I'd driven this skinny little idiot ten miles out of his way. And there still wasn't any motel key. "Okay, buddy, there you are. If he gives you any more trouble, have your dispatcher call our radio room and tell 'em you checked with us. Car forty-three sixty-two. He'll probably stay awake for a while, anyway. . . ."

"Yeah. I meant to ask how you got him to wake up so fast."

"Oh, that. Well, pain usually works pretty good—you dig your thumbnail into the inside of their earlobe, hard. Good luck with 'im!''

He was awake, all right. By the time I'd finished my U-turn to head him back toward where he belonged, he started bitching. "Holy good Jesus! What in shit are we doin' away to hell out here? Are you takin' me on a fuckin' tour, or what?"

I said, "Look, you miserable little creep! If you were any bigger'n a mouse fart, somebody would've torn your goddam head off and stuffed it up your ass forty years ago. So don't give me any more mouth, or I'll take care of that little chore *right now*! You read me?"

I guess he read me. The silence was beautiful—and he stayed awake. After about fifteen minutes we pulled up in front of the address that showed on his licence. He stared at the front door of the building for a minute and said, "Shit! I can't go in there . . . "

"Why the hell not? It's where you live, isn't it?"

"Well, yeah. Sort of . . . "

"What d'you mean, 'sort of'?"

"Well, she threw me out last week. Ten years—hell, *twelve* years—and she threw me out. Right on my ass."

I found it hard to be astonished. "So you *do* live in a motel . . . "

"Sure. I told you that, din't I?"

"Yeah, you told me that. You also told me you couldn't remember which one—and you've got no motel key. Why didn't you tell the cops? Why'd you let me drive you 'way up here? There's fourteen bucks on the meter already, and you're *still* not home."

"Fourteen bucks! You think I'm payin' *that*—for nothin'?"

"For nothing, hell! You ran it, you'll *pay* it!" I'm not much of a fighter, but I began to plan ways of tearing this little bastard into small pieces. Then, remembering the way assault charges usually go against cab-drivers, I decided to have one more go at trying to make some sense with this clown. I said, "Why don't you go in and see her? Maybe she's not mad any more."

"You kiddin' me? That broad's gonna stay mad for a hundred years! She'd bloody well *kill* me . . ."

So, okay — that angle wasn't going to work, and I'd had just about all I could take of this guy. (I made a mental note to find out more about that cop's trick with the ear and the thumbnail; it hadn't done a hell of a lot to improve his manners, but at least it had kept him awake for twenty minutes. That's a lot better than nothing, when you're running a drunk all over the place.)

" . . . and I still ain't payin' you no fourteen bucks!"

I think you probably have the picture by now. I had an hour or more invested in this pest, an urge to kill — and the knowledge, clear as icicles, that damned few judges are able to see the driver's side in an assault case. And the police *already* had my door number, sure as hell. Even radar cops write everything down.

I said, "Come on, chief. You look like a working stiff, just like me, and you know bloody well I've earned my money. Tell you what — lay a sawbuck on me for now, and we'll work the rest out when we get to your motel, okay?"

"Well, yeah. Sure. I guess so . . ." By the time I turned to look at him, the sonofabitch was sound asleep again. Enough is enough. I remembered his last name, from the glimpse of his driver's licence. What the hell? Let his wife kill him; it'd save me the trouble. I found his name on the apartment call-board and pushed the corresponding button. Three times — no answer. So, I wasn't going to get my money *that* way. I even tried the parade-square roar again; nothing.

I can get very stubborn about fourteen bucks; that's about half of my cost for a night's shift, including gas. Our dispatcher didn't waste any time; the cops were there in five minutes.

These two were a little less subtle than the radar cops; within twenty seconds I had a ten-spot in my hand and distinct orders to get him the hell out of their sight. And they'd found his motel key — it had slipped down between the cushions in the back seat. So away we went. Again.

It would have worked out fine, except that the little weasel had moved out of that particular motel three days before — without bothering to pay. This time, the motel manager called the cops. The silly part of the whole goddam scene was the fact that my fare carried a roll that would've choked a moose; it must've been well over a thousand dollars. I don't know what a psychologist would've made out of all this: the guy had plenty of money to pay his way almost anywhere, but he seemed to need abuse from some cop to make him pay it. Anyway, the motel manager got his money, did me the favour of making a few phone calls, and we headed—finally —to the motel we should've found two hours before.

One thing more (I figured you'd want to know this): there was twenty dollars on the meter, and he'd paid me ten at the apartment building. And guess what? He didn't want to pay me the rest of it. Apparently he'd overlooked one thing, though: the cops had been keeping track of all this bullshit, and I guess he wasn't any stranger to them. I made that one, final call to the dispatcher. Almost before I'd had a chance to hang up the mike, the prowl car was there.

Sure, I got my money. The cop even managed to find, in the midst of that enormous wad, a lottery ticket; one of the big ones. He handed it to me. "I can't steal a tip for you, but I got a rough idea of what this clown has taken you through tonight. Maybe this'll change your luck. *He*'ll never notice, for damn sure."

☞ CAPTAIN JACK AND THE LITTLE PEOPLE

☛ They say he was one of the finest smoke-eaters in the department, and I can't think of any reason to doubt that. Utterly fearless, they say: a man who'd stride into a building long after lesser men would have called the situation hopeless — and his crew would follow. They say his men felt safer inside a burning building—with Jack—than they did outside, without him.

And I've heard it said that the stuff of legends is belief, not believability; a legend can be a tale told by an idiot. It will announce itself, perhaps, by the small tingling it makes between the shoulder blades of the believer. A legend requires a hero, larger than life, and either a villain or a fool. . . .

I knew Jack fairly well. (That's not his real name, by the way; nor is it certain that he was a captain with the department, although I always assumed so.) A fine-looking man he was: well over six feet tall, taut as any athlete, and with a look of stern intelligence emphasized by a thrusting chin like the battering-ram prow of an ancient Greek warship. He *looked* like a leader of men; it is not at all difficult to imagine dozens of families, all over town, who owe their very lives to his vast courage and skill.

And he was a *nice* guy: friendly, easy to talk to, fittingly modest whenever anyone asked him about his fire-fighting career. He seemed to prefer not to talk about it at all. A hell of a man, really. A suitable hero, perhaps.

But wait:

Most firemen (they prefer to be called "firefighters") would probably go bananas if they didn't have jobs on the side. It's not strictly legal, but they all do it and everybody knows it; the authorities look the other way — until they're *forced* to notice. The practice dates back, of course, to the time when firemen were shamefully underpaid; now it's a result of boredom as much as anything else. A fireman's work schedule looks as if it had sprung from some mystical coupling of a ship's cook and a computer with half its parts missing. It goes something like this: seventy-two hours on duty — straight — and then ten days off. It varies in ways that defy all logic, and in permutations and combinations that would make an Einstein put a gun to his head. And imagine how many chores a wife could dream up in ten days!

So, the boys all take part-time jobs; and a lot of them have learned that the taxi business can be ideal for someone who works insane hours. It's easy work in most respects, usually pressure-free — and the money's worth while if you want to work at it.

Jack did. But he couldn't have made a worse choice of part-time jobs — for him.

I don't claim that cab-driving involves skills of a high order; but it does take some degree of intelligence to do it right, enough energy to grind out twelve-hour shifts — and some *luck*. And if luck was seagulls, Jack sure didn't need a hat.

Oh, he had *some* luck; everybody has. But if a car is a hostage to Fate, Jack was a hostage to the damned car. He got his share — or more — of airport shots and other goodies; he also managed to blow a transmission or a water pump or a tire on half of them. If there's one thing that no fare ever wants to know about, it's a taxi that doesn't go. Jack never talked about them, but I suspect he must've had some pretty spectacular confrontations with his passengers.

It would be easy to assume that the car was a piece of junk, but it's not that simple: the other drivers never had a second's trouble with it, and it always looked as if it had just come out of the showroom. And Jack is the only man I ever heard of who had *two* blow-outs in one day — after installing a whole new set of radials that very morning. Being a man of reason and perception, he might have imagined some awful Cosmic Purpose at the root of his daily disasters; being thoroughly Irish, he probably figured the Little People were out to screw him.

And then there were the dispatchers: they couldn't stand him.

There is a basic, almost holy, principle on which every dispatcher operates: when he calls for a car at a certain location, he must assume (there being no sane alternative) that the drivers responding to the call know what the hell they're doing. For the driver, that involves two things: knowing *exactly* where he is at every moment — and having a clear mental picture of the location (usually an intersection) the dispatcher is calling for. A good driver has a street map for a mind. So does a good dispatcher; it's his job to sort out the babble on the radio and find the car closest to the order. It sounds a lot simpler than it is.

Jack, unfortunately, could never remember where anything was. I've dispatched to him, and I know I could've sent him to the same street four times in a single shift — and have had to tell him where the hell the street was the *fifth* time. Dispatching taxis is an ulcer game at best, and there are several thoroughly nasty ways for a dispatcher to dump his frustrations on a driver who's not paying attention.

You ask: What might those ways be?

Well, there's always the old stand-by: thirty grocery runs in a row — but that's a bit primitive and obvious; most dispatchers prefer a more subtle approach. Like radio trouble: it can easily become impossible for the dispatcher to *hear* the offending car. Neat — and how the hell can you argue? And of course the miscreant could be sent twelve miles to pick up a fare that's just going around the corner; it's a method that many dispatchers prefer, for its symmetry. Human ingenuity is almost limitless, and

I'd guess that Captain Jack had reason to know all the ways.

He retired from the business three or four years ago, but not before the Little People had a final shot at him. Like many part-timers with good straight jobs and naive bank managers, Jack decided to buy his own package: plate, car, radio, meter. The going price was about twenty-four thousand.

The first thing he learned was that *all* cars hate him; his new car failed him and betrayed him in ways so spectacular, so vicious and cunning and catastrophic, that he could have been forgiven for wondering if the wheel had *really* been invented after all. But that wasn't the worst of it. He still held his job with the department, of course, which meant that he had to find *other* part-timers to drive his car when *he* couldn't.

Now the circle began to close, the stuff of legend began to emerge from the mists: hero, villain, fool — and victim. As if to purify him in the bright flame of inadvertence, the Fates (the Little People, perhaps?) took Jack as their own. The thrust of jaw became a little less imperial; the stern, intelligent gleam of eye became the look of a man haunted by horrors known and terrors yet to come.

It must've been at about this time that the Great Car-Wash Incident took place:

You'd check your windows very carefully before riding through a car-wash tunnel, wouldn't you? Of course you would; *anybody* would. I had just gassed up the car and taken it through the wash; I pulled over to one side and started to take a cloth to those parts of the windshield that the automatic wash always seems to miss. Suddenly, I heard Jack's voice — he'd been right behind me in the tunnel.

(I have to tell you that I've worked with — and lived among — soldiers, migrant tobacco-pickers, medical students, shipwrights, trombone players, and sports reporters; I had thought my vocabulary of obscenity reasonably complete. It seems it wasn't; Jack taught me a few beauts that night.)

The tunnel drive-chain nudged Jack's car the final two or three feet as I ambled over to see what all the yelling was about. It was pretty simple, actually: Jack sat, arms folded across his heroic chest, staring straight ahead from a face dark with rage. Every window in the car was wide open; it is not necessary to describe the scene any further.

Before I could open my mouth Jack said, in syllables carved from ancient ice, "Not a word. Not . . . one . . . fucking . . . word!"

That was just before things *really* started to go sour. His first part-time driver totalled the car by nudging the rear of a stopped streetcar—at forty miles an hour; which is about the same thing as adopting a law firm to support for the rest of your life. His second driver (no one will ever know how) managed to punch a car-sized dent in the side of a Swedish freighter tied up at Pier Eleven.

"The breaks of the game," some said. "These things happen." Sure they do. The bit with the freighter might defy statistical prediction, though. Jack finally determined that, for him, the profits from a part-time business tend to devour themselves. I think he got something like fifteen thousand for what was left of the whole mess; there wasn't any car. Fifteen thou' is a lot less than the plate was worth alone.

The breaks of the game? Jack had bought the package, replaced one car, and written off the replacement — and taken a nine-thousand-dollar kick in the head — all within a single month. Somebody was trying to tell him something.

You might say he went out in a blaze of abject surrender.

But, out there somewhere, fires wait to be fought, brave men to be led, lives to be saved. I'd like to think that Captain Jack survived the taxi business—somehow. He was a hell of a man, really.

# THE GOLD SHIRT

I thought I was a little too old to be impressionable, and I've certainly been around enough to be a bit cynical about a lot of things. But there can't be all that many perfect evenings in a summer: the temperature had been in the middle seventies all day, and dropped only a couple of degrees with the setting of the sun. The sky darkened from a bright green afterglow on the horizon to near-black overhead. The sight of Venus, like a welder's arc a millimetre from the moon, startled me when I turned west into the driveway.

There's a lot of talk about positive and negative ions — I don't remember which do what to whom — but the air was full of the good ones. My fare was waiting for me at the doors of the big apartment building.

She climbed in beside me, explaining that riding in the back made her car-sick, and started to chatter like an excited kid. Her husband was waiting for her at the Clinton, a lively place in the west end of town: drinks and dinner and dancing to a good group. Her holiday mood was so infectious — with the good ions doing their thing — that the trip was like a party. Just for the two of us.

She looked fantastic — a white linen suit with a skirt that accented the fine long legs; a little hat that couldn't possibly have looked that good on anyone else — and a smile to light up the whole car.

Her skin was the colour of rich chocolate.

I can't kid you. I go around fully equipped with all the standard prejudices, and I'm no better than average at trying to forget them. Let's just say I learned something that night: a beautiful woman is a beautiful woman. And colour be damned. The discovery shattered the hell out of a couple of pretty solid biases, and there's a good chance I made a bit of an ass of myself during that forty-minute trip. But we had a fine time. I've encountered charm, here and there; this girl had a patent on it. We pulled up in front of the Clinton in a lot less time than I would've wished.

People streamed in and out of the place, mostly blacks, all of them enjoying themselves. It took me a few seconds to figure out what was wrong here: everybody was smiling. Or laughing. And there wasn't a drunk in sight. I thought about the middle-class solemnity that hangs about most "white" bars like the stink of a glue factory next door.

"My husband'll pay you. I'm afraid I only have about a dollar with me." The meter read ten-eighty.

"Do you see him?" I began to wonder if I'd been taken in by one of the oldest tricks in the game — and hated myself for doubting her.

"No," she murmured, "he must be inside."

"He *is* expecting you, isn't he?"

"Oh, yes! He said he'd meet me at the door. I *know* he'll be here in a minute...."

We waited; perhaps three or four minutes. She began to twist the straps of her handbag, looking very small and very young. "I'd go in and look for him, but I just *hate* going into a bar by myself. Would you...?"

Would such a marvellous little doll do a number on me? Hell, what if she did? She had me right by the male ego. "Sure, dear. What's he look like?"

"Well, he's about six feet, with rimless glasses. And I think he's wearing his gold shirt... the one I gave him last birthday...."

The place was jumping — there must have been two hundred people moving in the heat and the noise and the drive of the hard rock music. I had trouble getting past the doorman until I explained. I couldn't find her husband; I got back in the car, a little ashamed of my surprise at finding her still there.

"You want to describe him again? He must be here...."

"Oh, I *know* he's here! He wouldn't let me down like this!"

(I guess not. *I* wouldn't.)

We waited another couple of minutes, not saying much. The holiday feeling was gone; she seemed on the verge of tears. Now what? You can't get ugly with a girl like this. It isn't the money, not really — it's the stupid, humiliating business of knowing you've been conned. It always feels worse when it's a woman.

Suddenly she brightened, waved, and began to bounce on the seat like a kid at the circus. "There he is! There he is!"

There he was, all right: six feet, rimless glasses — and the gold shirt.

As he walked toward the car I leaned across and whispered in her ear: "I think you forgot to tell me something...."

She stared at me, puzzled, while he counted out twelve dollars for the fare and tip. Then she burst into a bright peal of laughter that made my heart do a funny little flip — and gave me the happiest, sexiest wink I'd ever seen.

Her husband was very, very, very white.

☞ SOMETHING TO THINK ABOUT...

☞ Sam is a little annoyed.

We don't often see Big Sam annoyed, and it's something to think about. He's lying in a hospital bed that seems a couple of sizes too small for his huge frame, telling us about it.

They were just kids, maybe twenty or so, but full-grown and mean-drunk — and God knows what else they'd been popping along with the booze. Sam had just happened to cruise past the tavern, looking for a fare, when he found the three of them beating on Roy. Now, it must be said that Roy does have a way of leaving his mouth in Drive — when Park would be a much more discreet position at the time — but, what the hell, it doesn't take three punks to handle a guy like Roy, who is well into his forties and who would have to stand on a box to reach five-feet-three. And, bad odds or not, Roy *is* one of us, so Sam waded in to sort things out. He managed to drop two of them before the third one panicked and used the knife. Then they ran like hell. Sam says he'd know them anywhere.

The doctors say an average man might have bled to death, and with a little less luck the blade would've gone deeper. (Sam doesn't even remember feeling it at the time.) Right now the gash is ugly and sore, and going to be a lot sorer in a day or two: eighty-one stitches, from armpit to groin. Sam winces as someone cranks the bed up to a sitting position.

You have to celebrate the indestructibility of a legend (or a friend); the bottle of fine Scotch is passed around in the ritual of men congratulating themselves on a piece of good fortune. Someone had even thought to commandeer some plastic foam cups from the local Donut Hole.

A cute blonde nurse hurries into the room and fusses with one of the other patients, pretending to ignore the booze. Then she gives the act away by the disapproving little flip of her rump as she leaves. None of this is lost on Sam—I swear he did a week of healing, right then and there. Nobody doubts a nurse's ability to look after herself, but it's a safe bet that this one's defences will be put to the supreme test before Sam gets out of here.

They say he used to be married, working in a good trade, a real family man. Something changed all that, and I don't think I'd want to ask him about it. Right now I guess he's the freest man I know, in spite of the intentions of some of his favourite ladies.

Most big men look as if they'd been born big and just kept on growing; with Sam you get the impression he was carved, statue size, from scratch. It's a bit intimidating, but if he likes you he'll do just about anything to put you at ease. If he doesn't, it wouldn't make much sense to spend a lot of time in his company—especially when he decides to get into some serious partying.

The two-way radio makes us all buddies, especially on the night shift. I guess you could say it makes us responsible for each other, in a way. And Sam, just like the cavalry coming over the next hill, has a way of getting there when trouble happens.

The sight of Sam coming on the scene with blood in his eye—it seems to take about three seconds for all six-feet-six of him to unfold from his car—is usually enough to cool out all but the most vicious drunk. Still, every now and then some idiot decides to try him on for size. I've never heard of anyone trying it twice.

They tell stories about some of the brawls he's been in, but I think they miss the point. It's my guess that he doesn't really enjoy

fighting; it's simply that he feels his size gives him certain respon-
sibilities. He once told me, "I don't start fights . . . I stop 'em!"

Certainly his informal lectures on cause and effect (with appropriate demonstrations) have stopped a hell of a lot of unpleasantness
before it really got started.

This time it's different, though; this time Big Sam is a little
annoyed—someone failed to get the message. And somewhere out
there, there's a young man with a knife and a problem.

I wouldn't want to be him.

 BIOLOGY II

☛ I never feel obsolete—well, *almost* never—until I try to figure out why so many young chicks don't seem to mind the unending crap they take from their guys. I know the Pill stood the entire world on its ear (an interesting position, surely); but I don't think it was supposed to cauterize the minds of half the race's females between the ages of fourteen and twenty. Call me a chauvinist, but I prefer the time when girls were held, if not in awe, at least in enough respect that they didn't have to lug the beer.

He was about six-two, thick in the shoulders—and very, very cool. She was maybe eighteen, and pretty enough that she wouldn't often have to take second choice. I reached back and opened the right rear door for them. He slouched to the car, climbed in, and slammed the door. She hoisted the big case of beer up from the sidewalk with obvious effort and struggled around the back of the car to the other door, resting the beer on the trunk lid while she fumbled for the door handle. I opened it for her; she wrestled the case onto the seat and plopped down beside it.

Now, I know that the average, healthy woman can move pianos when there's no man around, if she has to, but I also know that the quality of life suffers when we let her do it. A two-four of beer probably weighs thirty pounds, tops, but it's a bloody awkward thing to handle.

The hulking oaf beside her didn't move an eyelash.

(None of my business, right? Right. In fact, I have a rule: If a woman is escorted by a man, I always let *him* make the helpful moves first; I step in only if I'm needed. It's the way I'd prefer it— if *I* were the escort.)

We headed east, to an address a couple of miles down the road. Neither of them uttered a sound; it must've been a real fun party they were going to. Finally I wheeled into a driveway that stopped about a hundred feet from the house. Her hero climbed out of the car and headed up the hill toward the house without a backward glance, while she tried to heave the case of beer to her shoulder. I couldn't take any more of it; I took the beer case from her hands and carried it up to the house. The oaf had disappeared inside. She counted out the fare in silver and pennies.

I had to ask: "Forgive me if I sound like a father, dear, but why the hell do you chicks let these big clowns treat you the way they do . . . and I bet you paid for the beer *too*, didn't you?"

She seemed surprised: "Yes, I did. He's broke this weekend."

I made a mental bet with myself that he was broke *every* weekend. I said: "Even so, how come *you* have to carry the beer? He's big enough to carry a truck. Why do you let them get away with it?"

She looked puzzled: "Let them get away with what? I don't think I know what you mean. . . ."

"Come *on*, dear! You don't think the guys should carry the heavy stuff . . . maybe open doors once in a while?"

"Oh, I don't think they'd want to do that. . . ."

"Why not? Guys *used* to do it, all the time. *I* just did, remember?"

"Yeah. Thanks. But . . ."

"But the whole idea is so old-fashioned that it embarrasses you a little, right? And I don't mean just you . . . I mean *most* of you young chicks."

She stirred a few blades of grass with her foot, looking very young and very vulnerable. She said, "I think I know what you're talkin' about. . . . My mother keeps telling me stuff like that. I feel dumb, carryin' the beer and all that, but some of the guys just won't . . . and what the hell can *we* do about it?''

"What can you *do*? You mean you don't know?"

She laughed. (You don't often hear one of these young 'uns laugh quite the way she did.) "You mean, just quit putting-out for them? Yeah, we could do that. But would it be *honest*?"

"Maybe not, but a hell of a lot of spoiled little boys would grow up awful fast."

With that, her hero's voice boomed through the open front screen-door from somewhere in the back of the house: "Sheila! Haul ass in here and bring that fuckin' beer! Now!"

Sheila tried to tuck the big box of beer under one arm and fumbled with the door latch with her other hand. She almost dropped the box once or twice, but I was damned if I'd help this time. There was a ray of hope, though: the look on her face suggested that this night—just maybe—her hero was about to learn something of value: something about growing up.

After all, they haven't repealed biology, have they?

☞ BRING ON
THE CLOWNS

☛ I'm a customer too, sometimes. And I don't always like what I see, especially when I happen to hail one of the piles of iron that prowl the downtown streets.

It's hot. The black heat of the asphalt seems to drive up through the floor of the car, bringing with it the stink of ten thousand dreary trips: traces of God knows what mixture of perfumes, the stale and bitter scent of forgotten cigars, hints of desperate and hastily cleaned-up vomitings. The driver is an indeterminate forty (or sixty); thinning hair greased straight back; skinny, and with a face that reflects the fact that its owner would obviously rather be doing just about anything else but driving hack. At least he's cleaner than the car. The rubber mats are worn through, the vinyl covering the dashboard is ripped, and the car rides like a lumber wagon through a mine-field. The Tariff Card, clipped to the right-hand visor, reveals that this piece of junk is owned by something called Modern Investments (1967) Inc.

"Who do you drive for, friend?"

He looks at me suspiciously, then: "Hell, I dunno. All I know is , I go over to Harry's Garage every morning and they gimme a car."

"You don't drive the same car every day?" (I know the answer.)

"No, and I ain't drivin' this shit-box again. No way."

"Yeah. Kind of baffed, isn't it?"

"Hah!" he snorts. "Harry's got a couple over there even worse

than this. I already told 'im he gives me a decent set of wheels or I
quit. But they're *all* shit . . . I dunno how he gets away with it.''

☛ How is this possible? How *does* Harry get away with it? There
is, after all, an Inspection Office charged with the responsibility of
protecting the public from mobile death-traps — and from drivers
who might wish to indulge in a bit of rape or other thuggery from
time to time.

The Office handles part of its mandate with efficiency: it's
almost impossible to get a cab-driver's licence if your record
reveals anything much heavier than forgetting to return a library
book. There are some bums in the business — but damned few
convicted hoods. In fact, the Office checks you out at each annual
renewal of your licence.

There's no equivalent control over who *owns* the cabs in this
town, however. It's pretty widely accepted that about a quarter of
the plates are owned by people who have never even *visited* this
country — and there's a strong suspicion that the Mafia is not
without a toe-hold in the business. (Why not the Mafia? Its laun-
dered money buys cabs in almost every big city in North America.)
If you live, say, in Tel Aviv, or Frankfurt, or Buenos Aires, there's
no real problem to realizing a return from your investment in a few
taxis here: you just find a reliable garage operator (or lawyer) who
will manage them for you, for a percentage of the take. He will
keep expenses—especially maintenance expenses—to an absolute
minimum and will see to it that you earn about sixteen per cent on
your investment. That's a pretty comfortable return — and you
don't even have to know what *colour* your cars are.

☛ The Inspection Office took over regulation of the taxi industry
from the police about twenty years ago. It was a neat political
move, and it created a couple of hundred comfortable jobs. (Nobody will talk about it at the Office, but I believe that *one* employee
has actually driven hack for a living.) At least the police knew who

all the crooks were; the Office doesn't seem to know much about anything.

Item: A good friend of mine — an honest, compassionate man and the owner of about a dozen cabs—has gathered the impression that it's in his best interests to deliver, a couple of times a year, a case of the best Scotch to appropriate flunkeys employed by the Office. He hates the idea, but he's far from stupid. The reason is that each of his cars must pass a safety inspection three times a year; that amounts to about forty inspections a year — and a failed inspection costs money. So he delivers the Scotch, alert to the strong possibility that gentlemen with larger operations may deliver something even more substantial; after all, *some* cabs have to fail the inspections, or it wouldn't look right. Would it?

Item: It's the driver's job—traditionally and usually without pay — to take the cab through the periodic inspections, a process that can take anywhere from an hour to a full day. The inspectors (in theory, at least) look for safety, general appearance and cleanliness of the car, and accuracy of the meter.

On one memorable occasion I pulled into the inspection bay half expecting (hell, I was *hoping*) the inspectors would rip the plates off the piece of junk I was driving and leave it outside to finish rotting.

The damned thing passed with flying colours.

To be absolutely fair to the Office—it hurts—I have to admit that Transport Department inspectors handle the mechanical end of the check; the Office people look for things like general appearance, proper licensing, and so on. But I swear that it often looks as if they're all in it together; as if the Transport people know which cabs are coming through that day — and which ones the Office wants passed, no matter what.

Anyway, I insisted on a re-inspection; it shook hell out of them. The second time through, they managed to find *twenty-one* faults in that bucket; and still they let me drive it away—with a notice for the owner, giving him two days to get it fixed. An interesting detail: he fired me when I handed him the notice. I guess his cars weren't *supposed* to fail inspection.

☛ Sometimes it works the other way, as if the special demons of this nutty business have to keep reminding us they're still at work. Like the time I took in Al's car. This was a good car, maybe six months old and running like a watch. The owner was a master mechanic, and this one was the special baby of his little fleet. It had received constant and expert care since the day he'd driven it from the show-room: and I never thrash a car. Never.

Some day I hope to understand why cushy government jobs make so many of their owners so goddam miserable. (Imagine being a mechanic who never has to *fix* anything.) This one, the Transport Department inspector — tall and skinny and with a face like a smacked ass—failed the car on a faulty left lower ball-joint.

Al exploded when I got back to the garage: "Bullshit! Absolute crap! No goddam way is there anything wrong with that car!" He stared at the inspection sheet, cursing, then hauled a new ball-joint down from the top shelf in the stockroom. "Look at that! Feel it!" I hefted the new part in my hand and rattled the ball around in its socket.

"That's the way the damn things are *made*, for godsake... three-thirty-seconds play in 'em... the grease takes up the slack." Al crouched under the hoist, wrapping big hands around various parts of the front end of the car, twisting and tugging, trying to find any looseness. "No way! There's just nothin' wrong with her. Tell you what.... Go back out and run it past those clowns again. I'll give you twenty bucks for your time... hell, I'll give you *thirty* if you can bluff your way through!"

I got my thirty. Less than three hours after he'd failed it, the same, sour inspector passed the car — complete with the old ball-joint.

I suppose there are times when public safety is served, when a beat-up, dirty, unsafe cab has the plates ripped off it — quite properly, wisely, and efficiently. It may even happen to cars whose owners have the right connections downtown. But not often.

☛ There are just over two thousand cabs in the city; about half of them—most in the big downtown fleets—are barely safe for a trip of a few blocks. Some of them were ripe for the scrap heap two years ago; and all this in spite of the mandatory three inspections a year (as well as occasional, casual spot-checks by mobile teams of Office inspectors), and in spite of the fact that no car over five years old is allowed to stay on the road as a taxi. The spot-checks, of course, are a joke: the *real* purpose of the exercise is to see if the driver might be fiddling the trip-sheet. They have nothing to do with safety.

Every now and then someone tries to find out who really *owns* the cabs in this town. If, as some people suspect, the Mafia has an interest in the business, the question becomes important. And if, as many customers suspect, too many taxis are run-down and filthy— perhaps even dangerous — the answer to that question should be public property.

You can, with relatively little effort, obtain a list of all the brain surgeons in the country, all the clergymen, all the psychologists, all the nuclear physicists, all the druggists. You *cannot* obtain a list of the cab owners in this city. It's been tried more than once; a couple of years ago a respected, *elected* member of the Inspection Office demanded access to the owners' list — a list of the very people he was expected to regulate—and was turned down by the flunkeys in the Office. As far as I know, he never did see the owner's list.

The ultimate bureaucracy, surely. Think about that — the next time you place your valuable butt on the back seat of a taxi that looks a little ratty.

☞ A LONELY WAY TO DIE

☞ You don't always get a chance to know how good your luck really is. I found out about mine — from a cop. But I'm getting a little ahead of the story.

Fact: There are places in this world where a kid just naturally grows up with a razor in his shoe—perhaps because he has to—and graduates to a gun at about fourteen. With luck, he'll outgrow the need for these virility totems; but in those places life is cheap, and luck is not.

It's possible that judges and politicians and editorial-page writers don't know this. The splendid isolation of a Rosedale or a Forest Hill can reduce gut-spilling violence to a statistic, the victim's terror to a neat exercise for the psychologists. But there's nothing neat or academic about threats, or a beating, or a gun held to your head. It's not something you can contemplate over a good Scotch while you plan your next legal move. Ask any cop—or cab-driver. A lot of us have been there.

☞ The three of them were black and arrogant and stoned, almost caricatures of the old hostilities. I won't claim I came off any better than they did; all my defences were up. But I wasn't about to mount a crusade when they finally got out of my cab, leaving three doors hanging open, two-fifty on the meter — and my blood pressure raging.

Not being paid is one of the hazards of the business. Sometimes you can do something about it; sometimes you can't. Learning the difference is one of the survival techniques, and at three to one I'm no hero. It was a busy Friday night, one of those nights when you can take home seventy or eighty dollars after expenses. It took me a while to get those three punks out of my system, but if you'd asked me at the end of the shift where I'd lost two-fifty, I couldn't have told you.

☛ Saturday night was more of the same, perhaps busier. It was about ten-fifteen before I had a chance to stop and think about anything. I drove to a post, told the dispatcher where I was, and leaned back to relax for a minute.

With tha⁺, the dispatcher said, "Hold it, guys. I got trouble." Some new driver either hadn't heard or didn't know any better. He started to chop up the air with something that didn't matter much.

"I said hold it, for chrissake! Now shut up!" Ron sounded worried. "Now, what was that, Four-two?" Silence. "I *know* you called me, Four-two . . . where are you?"

More silence.

The back of my neck tingled, and I know another hundred guys felt the same way. Saturday night is nut night.

"Four-two . . ." The dispatcher held the mike open for a couple of extra seconds, and I could hear the phone ringing on his desk. (Ordinary calls don't come through that phone.) Then the whole frequency seemed to go dead.

After a minute or two—it seemed much longer—he came back on the air. I hardly recognized his voice, and I've known Ron for years.

"Okay, guys. Listen. The police called about one of our cars in trouble somewhere on Golf Club Road. If anybody's close to it—I mean *close* —have a look and let me know. Otherwise I want this frequency kept clear. Understand? Clear! I don't want to hear from *anybody* . . . unless it's about Golf Club Road!"

The radio went dead again. I thought about the long, narrow road winding through a hollow that could be a hundred miles from the city, bisecting a posh golf course and finding its way over a stone bridge out of another century: a warm, green place in the first light of a summer sun—and a dark, lonely place on a March night.

Suddenly: "There he is! There's the car . . . right by the bridge." I could hear sirens behind the voice. Then, "Oh Jesus! Looks like blood all over . . ."

Ron came back. "What's happening, guys? Can you help him?"

"There's cop cars all over the place . . . just a minute. . . . Nahh! There's about ten of us here and they won't let us near him!" (Indistinct shouts in the background, another siren.)

"Okay. Let me know when you find out something." Silence again, two or three minutes.

The other voice said, "They're putting him in the ambulance now. Looks like he's been shot! *Shot!*"

Everybody tried to talk at once, and two-way radios aren't built for that; it sounded like a bunch of apes blowing whistles. Finally Ron sorted it out: "Is he alive?"

"Yeah. I think so . . ."

"Who is it, Harry? I think his first name's Gord."

"Yeah. Gord . . . Stoddart? That's it, Stoddart."

"Okay, Harry. Thanks." Ron sounded beat, a long way from his usual style. Nobody else had anything to say.

☛ It's hard to describe the rest of that night:

The frantic bursts of activity when the dispatcher was able to get a few orders out over the air; the anger of the customers who'd had to wait too long, not knowing; the people at corners and bus stops, trying desperately to flag down a cab, any cab (I doubt that many of them had much luck, that night); the long periods of silence on the radio.

The silence was the worst part of it. I can't tell you how weird that feels, especially when the night is already charged with trouble.

Descriptions began to filter through the grapevine and over the air: three young men, possibly black, probably still armed. And very likely trapped within a mile radius of the shooting. Small clusters of cabs gathered on posts and at donut shops and restaurants, the drivers exchanging news and suspicions, then driving off — either to work or to park their cabs in a vague kind of despair.

I don't claim that Gord had been everybody's pal, or that we all felt a shattering sense of loss. Hell, he only drove on weekends to make a few extra bucks, and I don't think half the guys in the fleet had ever met him. But goddam it, he was one of *ours*; we had the right to resent what had happened to him, and we did.

That night the battle lines were drawn a little tighter around us and against the random brutality that we seem to spend too much of our time dealing with. There was some talk about how we should all start to carry weapons, and the law be damned. But that's all it was: talk. Any cop will tell you that the best way to get shot is to let everybody know you carry a gun yourself.

The thing I remember most about that long, fitful night was the feeling of suspended reality, the sullen business of just going through the motions. It wasn't outrage, not yet. It was a helpless, formless disgust — and being shown, again, how close the jungle really is to the city.

I guess it must have been about one in the morning when the dispatcher interrupted a string of orders to tell us the hospital had called: Gord was dead. I had to pull over to the side of the road to think about it. I remembered something Gord had said, the one time I met him over coffee with a few of the guys: "Get thumped or wasted for a few lousy bucks? No way! The bastards can have it."

I tried to imagine how he must have felt during that last minute, driving down that dark winter road to nothing, with three hostile punks in the back seat. Did he know his life was almost over — or did it all happen without a second's warning?

We'll never know.

And I thought: What a meaningless, filthy, lonely way to die.

We learned, later, that the bastards hadn't even robbed him. They blew half of his head away, just for the hell of it. Because a gun always gets used—sooner or later.

☛ There were several sequels to the doings of that strange March night:

The cops towed Gord's car to a police garage and kept it there almost a week, checking bone fragments embedded in the dashboard, testing blood stains, checking for prints; they kept whatever they knew about the shooting to themselves. And they were just a little friendlier to us, for a while.

The newspaper editorials, full of reason and white-collar indignation. The anguished statements of local politicians. The roaring silence on the part of the Inspection Office, that splendid — and politically appointed — watchdog of sanity and safety in the cab business.

And the funeral: a story in itself. Drivers attended from as far away as Minneapolis.

My own sequel came several days after the shooting, after the police had done whatever the police do to get a case rolling:

A few of us were having our usual midnight beer and de-briefing at the Suburban. When a cop came to our table I suppose everybody wondered, "Shit! What've I done now?" But he just wanted us to have a look at a thing called an "Information"—a kind of tip-sheet on current projects in Police-land: details of the crime, statistics on the suspects, mug shots if they have them. In short, a work-order for the cop on the street. This one was about the Stoddart murder.

The sheet passed around the table to me. For some reason, I looked at the ages first: fifteen, sixteen, nineteen. I read on: hard drugs, weapons, B. and E., assault. Nice kids. Then the photos— three black youngsters. My ears rang, and I wouldn't have wanted to try to stand up, just then.

They hadn't looked like kids a week ago—in the back seat of my cab.

☞ THE NIGHT CHARLIE GOT THE BLOOD

☛ Almost everybody calls him Crazy Charlie — not to his face, necessarily — and they may be right. I really wouldn't want to say for sure, but I have a hunch that, of all the things Charlie may be, crazy isn't one of them.

I do know he's a displaced Maritimer; maybe he's just not programmed to worry about some of the things that perplex and harass the rest of us. Crazy or not, Charlie is some kind of driver.

Fate seems to take a special interest in Charlie. Not that his luck is especially good — it isn't, but that's another story — it's as if unseen Powers were preparing him for some awful transmutation, rehearsing him for a state of being in which the laws of gravity and probability will no longer apply to him.

Charlie is special. If ten improbable, grotesque, or tragic things are going to happen during a single shift, with fifty of our cars working, it's a safe bet that at least eight of those things will happen in Charlie's car, or somewhere near it. If he kept a diary, a typical Saturday night shift might read something like this:

8:00 p.m.	Witnessed bad collision. Assisted until arrival of police, four ambulances.
9:10	Attacked by vicious drunk. Police.
10:30	Maternity run. Woman's pains thirty seconds apart on arrival at hospital.
11:45	Attacked by drunk with no money. Police.

1:00 a.m.   Female passenger, about eighteen. Badly cut and
            bruised. Says boyfriend beat her, refuses to go to
            hospital.
2:15   Hysterical woman passenger, doesn't know where
            going. Police.
4:00   Lost patience, attacked vicious drunk with no money.
            No police.

You might suspect that such a diary — if Charlie kept one —
would be full of exaggerations, but this would not be the case.
Charlie is so inured to these interruptions and distractions that he
would consider them unworthy of embellishment. He simply nar-
rates them over the radio, often as they are actually happening, and
we all hear almost every word of what's going on. It never occurs to
us to question the accuracy of his little narratives. We know him.

Like the time he got the blood . . .

I guess it was about two in the morning; there certainly wasn't
much happening. A few of the guys were sitting in my car outside
Millie's, drinking coffee and listening to the silence on the radio.

Suddenly, "I need a car downtown. Anybody downtown?"

The dispatcher's voice had an odd note of urgency about it. We
all sat up a little straighter.

"Downtown, please. I gotta have a car downtown!"

None of us reached for the mike; we were about as far from
downtown as you can get.

The radio crackled. We couldn't hear the words, but it was
Charlie's voice, miles away.

"What's that?" The dispatcher's voice, loud and clear.

The speaker crackled again. Charlie.

"Okay, Charlie. Head it down to the blood bank on St. Patrick
Street."

More crackling and hissing.

"Yeah, I'll see if I can get you an escort. Put your foot in it,
Charlie. Call me when you pick up the blood."

We sat and talked for a while, mostly about the goofy things that happen to Charlie. We figured he'd be on the parkway now, just smoking it along—we all knew how he drives when he's in a hurry.

It couldn't have been more than five or six minutes before the dispatcher came back on the air.

"What's that, Charlie? Already?"

Faint rustling. We couldn't make out Charlie's voice at all.

"Okay. You know where it's going? Right. Back out here to the Centenary Hospital."

We finished our coffee; one of the guys went back into the restaurant and brought out another round. We hadn't finished these when Charlie came roaring into the parking lot with a shriek of brakes and an enormous grin on his face.

With that the dispatcher's voice, a little worried, came through the speaker. "Where are you now, Charlie? I've got the doctor on the phone."

"I'm gettin' you a coffee."

"For godsake, Charlie! The blood! Where's the blood?"

"You kiddin' me? I delivered it a couple minutes ago. Tell the doc' to call downstairs and shake them up a bit. How do you take your coffee?"

The dispatcher said something that shouldn't have gone over the air. I guess he hit the mike switch with his elbow, or something.

Taxi orders are time-stamped when they come in, so it was possible to reconstruct the whole episode. The hospital had first phoned at 2:02. Within a few seconds Charlie was on his way, from a point about six miles from the blood bank. Rather than try to escort Charlie, the police had placed cruisers to block the important side streets along the route. Charlie remembers running a dozen red lights — and I remember looking at my watch when he came wheeling into the restaurant.

Exactly 2:30.

In twenty-eight minutes he had driven approximately thirty-two miles, much of it through narrow city streets. It had taken him a minute or so to pick up the blood, perhaps another minute to drop it at the other end. And a couple of minutes to drive from the hospital to Millie's.

The patient lived, by the way. During that twenty-eight minutes, he had been stretched out on the operating table, as open as a rifled purse, while the surgeon waited for the blood.

I would say that man owes Charlie a drink, some time.

 TOUGH GUY

☛ There's nothing mysterious about the Bullshit Barrier; I suppose every in-group has its own version of the same thing. It's the unspoken rule that keeps exaggeration, among friends, within tolerable limits—most of the time.

Steve might have been forgiven for trying to break the Barrier almost every time he opened his mouth, if he had occasionally bought a round when his turn came. It is not noted that he ever refused a drink when someone *else* was buying. His other social error was only slightly less glaring: he made it very plain that he was in the business only long enough to get his hands on some quick cash—a few weeks at most—and that the rest of us were a bunch of clowns for hanging in there as if it were our living, or something.

Steve was the only man I'd ever met who could swagger sitting down. His conversation was an endless recounting of inferred slights to his manhood, instantly avenged, of course; bar-room brawls of awesome proportions; and tumid, tumbled episodes with eager girls in the back seats of restored '57 Chevies.

If he thought his stories were entertaining enough to pay his dues into the gang, they weren't — and they didn't. You can't con (or amuse) cab-drivers with tales of your prowess in brawls or back seats, particularly after you've proclaimed your amateur standing as a driver.

For one thing, we don't need to get our violence second-hand; the business attracts more than its share. For another, there's no lack of sexual opportunity; a lot of it isn't especially enticing, but it's there. And everybody knows that trying it in a car is like attacking a steak with a plastic spoon: you're so busy with the details that you can't enjoy the effect. Worse, it lacks class.

I don't think any of the guys ever paid the slightest attention to anything Steve said.

When he listened — which was seldom enough — you knew he was just waiting for that one word, the ultimate insult, that would ignite the fires of revenge deep down in that strange, *macho* image he had of himself. The trouble was, he didn't know whether he was Marshal Dillon — or pure, red-neck Tennessee truck-driver.

Steve's appearance was remarkable only for the fact that you seldom see greased, sculptured hair these days. You noticed his eyes, too — small, hooded, and suspicious. He was maybe five-ten and of rather slight build — which he tried to disguise by walking with his elbows held about four inches out from his sides.

Everything considered, he had all the charm of a stone in a snowball. And somehow, somewhere, he got the idea I was his friend; God knows, the rest of the guys couldn't stand him. Anyway, he soon learned where and when I made a habit of having lunch or dinner, or a few beers after work — and there he'd be, waiting for me, almost every time.

At my age I find a chip on the shoulder more curious than threatening, so I went along with it for a while. I wanted to find out what made Steve tick.

I still don't know.

Once in a while I managed to get past the thick shell of arrogance — and found nothing but rock-stubborn ignorance. I tried to find out whether the ignorance was real, or just another of his defences; and there just wasn't any way to tell.

A psychiatrist might say: "Certainly! What the hell did you expect? Leave the nuts to us shrinks . . . you'll live longer!"

I'm no shrink. I finally just wanted to get away from Steve, as far and as fast as I could. But the whole thing soon became academic.

☛ It was 6:30. The taverns were disgorging their swarms of late-afternoon drunks.

The driver's voice came through the radio too loudly; frightened, and quite near by.

"Car Seven . . . I got a problem at the Gerrard House . . ." The mike stayed open for a few more seconds, and I could hear other voices in the background, gruff and threatening.

Then, Steve: "I'm just a couple blocks away. I'll have a look." It was the first time I'd ever heard Steve on the air, other than to make money.

My fare was dubious. I had to make some fancy financial arrangements with her, including taking a couple of dollars off the meter price, before she'd let me drive the few blocks out of the way to see what was happening with car Seven.

We pulled up in front of the tavern just as Steve let go a looping right that flattened one of the drunks. Another leaned against the building, blood streaming from his nose.

The car Seven driver stood to one side. Roy is roughly the size of a starving jockey, and certainly no match for two burly drunks. His hand shook so that he could hardly hold the match to his cigarette.

Steve walked over to me, grinning—and white as a sheet.

"I got 'em," he yelled. "I got the bastards!"

"Yeah, you got 'em," I said. "You sure as hell did!"

With that, the police cruiser rolled in, the siren moaning down the scale to a low growl.

Steve was shouting again: "Nobody pushes *my* buddies around . . . no fuckin' way!"

Then he passed out, right on the sidewalk, cold as a mackerel. Roy and I looked at each other; the cop looked at all three of us. The confusion was cleared up in a few seconds, and the cop wrestled the two drunks into the back seat of the cruiser. Just as he walked back toward us, Steve began to stir.

"I'm real curious about this," the cop said as we helped Steve to his feet.

"You okay?" I asked Steve.

"Yeah, I'm okay . . . but I think I want to be sick." When he took a few deep breaths some of his colour returned. He grabbed my arm for a second or two, then asked for a cigarette. I lit a couple and handed one to him.

"Whenever you're ready, gentlemen. . . ." The cop was getting a little impatient. Steve and Roy followed him to the cruiser, so I drove off with my fare. I'd almost forgotten her.

☛ It takes maybe an hour for a story like this to spread among a hundred drivers.

By the time the usual suspects — about a dozen of us — had checked into the Suburban for a midnight beer and sandwich, everyone had his own version of what had happened at the Gerrard House. Guys who must have been thirty miles away at the time became eyewitnesses, practically. I just drank my beer.

Nobody commended Steve, really—not in so many words—and nobody knocked him, either. Maybe tonight he'd finally paid his dues. Now he'd owe us a round, for sure.

☛ Perhaps you've guessed.

We never saw Steve again, never heard from him — except for one postcard, addressed to me through the office:

Hey suckers.
I stil say your in the wrong bussines. Driving the big rigs is where its at.
But serously I miss the gang and beers at Suburban say hello to all my good buddys. Regards Steve.

I'm goddamned if the thing wasn't postmarked somewhere in Tennessee.

☞ THE GIRLS

☞ The phenomenon isn't quite new enough to be a spin-off from Women's Lib, but it's taking a long time to lose its shock value: Women Driving Cabs.

I doubt that the Movement has bothered to involve itself in the taxi business; if it has, our girls don't talk about it. I suspect the militants know that their best newspaper mileage comes from demanding — loudly — that bosses learn to fetch their own coffee and dry-cleaning.

Each of our girls is *her own* freedom-fighter. Together, they'd probably drive the libbers stark raving.

☞ Jane reminds you of sailboats and horseback-riding and good schools. She's built like a model, which is to say that another fifteen pounds would make her a very pretty young woman. I've learned to be sure of my facts before getting into heavy discussions with her; Jane has done plenty of reading of her own.

Q: Jane, did you borrow the money to buy your cab, or did your father buy it for you?

A: That's a damn strange question! I'm not sure I like it.

Q: Sorry. But I have a reason for asking. *Did* your father set you up? It's a big investment . . .

A: For a female, you mean. Go ahead. Say it.

Q: It's a big investment for *anybody*, Jane. I wasn't patronizing you.

A: Okay. I guess I'm being too sensitive. No, Daddy didn't set me up. He might've helped me buy a dress shop, or something like that—but not this. He's still not crazy about the idea. But I had a little money of my own . . . and I borrowed the rest. From the bank, just like anyone else.

Q: You look like a girl who could be doing just about anything she wanted to. Why this?

A: You mean, what's a nice girl like me doing driving a hack? Sorry . . . it's just that I've heard it so often.

Q: I understand. Even so, you've gone about twenty-five thousand into debt . . .

A: A little more than that, actually. That's a new Olds sitting out there.

Q: Well, whatever.

A: Call it a challenge. Maybe I did it to show my father I *could* do it. At least I have a business of my own . . . I'll never have to depend on anybody.

Q: Don't you ever think about getting married, having kids?

A: Hell, no!

Q: Bitter?

A: Perhaps. Just a bit.

Q: And you'd rather not talk about it.

A: Right on!

Q: Okay, then. How's the business going for you? Are you making money?

A: I will be, if I can ever get the goddam car running the way it should. It's been one bloody thing after another.

Q: Is that your biggest expense . . . repairs?

A: It shouldn't be, but that's the way it's been working out.

Q: Why did you buy a big, heavy car like that?

A: Oh, I thought it would be more fun to have a little luxury while I work. After all, the car's my office, my living room . . .

Q: I suppose that's true . . . with the hours you must put in.

A: Yes, but I'm learning the hard way. These big cars are all power and smooth ride. No beef where it really matters . . . and the price of parts is murder. Next time I'll buy a smaller car. The customers sure as hell don't notice.

Q: I guess not. Well, what would *ordinarily* be your heaviest expense?

A: Oh, the bank payments, of course! Over a hundred and sixty dollars every Monday morning. But that won't be forever . . . unless I decide to buy another when this one's paid for.

Q: You mean you'd do this again?

A: Maybe. We'll see. . . .

Q: You are one gutsy lady, Jane. How much do you figure you have to take in every week?

A: Let me think. Well, there's the bank payment . . . we've got that . . . then gas and oil, say another hundred at least, I budget seventy-five a week for repairs, and it never seems to be enough. Insurance, about forty. How about twenty for emergencies and licence fees?

Q: Is that everything?

A: It can't be. Let me see . . . oh! I almost forgot brokerage dues and rent for the radio. Make that another forty. And I like to put aside about thirty . . . for when I have to replace the car.

Q: That's . . . hmm . . . good grief! That's over four-fifty a week!

A: Yeah. Scary, isn't it?

Q: So, to make a decent living, you have to take in about seven hundred dollars a week. Can you do it?

A: Yes, usually. *If* I work an eighty-hour week, or put a part-time driver on the car for a few shifts a week. But some weeks I can't . . . so I cheat.

Q: Cheat? How?

A: Oh, I just forget about putting anything in the kitty for the new car . . . or hope I don't have any repairs for a while. Or hope that my bank manager is still speaking to me.

Q: And you'd do it all again?
A: I might. I just might.
Q: But why, Jane? A young woman in a business like this . . .
A: Because it's freedom, and I love it. I just love it!

☞ I have this theory:

The really good ones get even better, after thirty. (I think most of us knew that long before the hair-colouring manufacturers' ad agencies caught on to it.)

Edie is well into the good years, and comfortable with herself. Not that she's all sweetness and light; hell, she can teach most people a thing or two about how to hold up their end of an argument. But Edie is all woman, and if one thing drivers her it is the utter refusal to take any bullshit from anyone — her husband, especially.

Edie and Doug and I have been good friends for years, and it's taken most of those years to reach the understanding that I will *not* referee any more of their arguments. That sounds easier than it is. Doug has a way of walking straight into her verbal ambushes.

The rumour-mill in this business is downright fearsome. I'll never understand how grown men and women—with a living to be made, the hard way — can manage to spend so much time and energy speculating about each other. Not everyone in the game is a gossip, of course; it just seems that way. I'm absolutely convinced that if you wait long enough, and listen at the right places, you'll eventually hear any rumour you want to hear. About anybody, even yourself.

Doug and Edie have been through the mill a few times, but rather less since they got together a couple of years ago. (It's hard to cook up stories about a happy couple.) Even so, the rumours still surface once in a while. The world being the way it is, Doug's alleged exploits just serve to confirm his virility—if not his discretion. To

Edie's great credit, she simply ignores the stories about herself—and about Doug. It can't be easy; some of them are pretty raunchy.

The point I want to make is that Edie has the kind of class that carries her above all the crap that a few gristle-brained clowns would have you believe about her.

Maybe it's class that lets Edie tell me:

"Trouble? I don't have any trouble."

"You mean you've never had anyone give you a hassle in the cab?"

"Not really. Well, that depends on what you mean. . . . Some fares can be a real pain in the ass, of course . . . "

"Okay, let's start with that. Who gives you the most aggravation? Drunks?"

"No . . . they don't usually bother me, and I don't bother them. Oh, there's been the odd one I've had to put out of my car, but not many." (Edie is about four-feet-ten. She must use some pretty convincing language to get them out.)

"Who, then?"

"Snotty women. They're the ones who really get me steaming."

"Oh? How's that?"

"Well, some of these bitches have never done a day's work in their lives . . . their idea of sweat is putting a couple of hundred dollars on their old man's charge-cards . . . and they love to go into the Mother Superior routine."

"Mother Superior?"

"Sure. Haven't you ever noticed? Got to keep the servants in their place, you know."

"And you're one of the servants?"

"Of course. At least to the extent I really *exist* to them, I'm a servant. Menial type."

"You must be a surprise to a lot of them . . . do you have many women ask you why you're driving a taxi?"

"A few. Well, what they do is make a statement that only *sounds* like a question. They don't really want to know."

"That seems odd."

"Not if you know women. We're not real great listeners, you know."

"That can't explain the whole thing, though. . . ."

"No, it can't. I think maybe I represent a threat to some of these broads. I screw up their idea of what their femininity is all about. They *have* to resent me."

"That sounds as if Women's Lib has a long way to go. Or is that a fair statement?"

"Oh, it's fair enough. I wish it wasn't. We just have to wait till the whole mink-coat thing dies off."

I wish I'd said that.

☛ Let's meet Chris.

She's about twenty-five and looks younger; long chestnut hair frames a pixie face that smiles a bit too seldom, and that's the world's loss. The women's magazines would call her petite. The same magazines might fail to mention that she is one hell of a cook, with great legs—and a mind like a steel trap.

Chris is divorced, with no visible regrets about it.

Q: What's a nice girl like you doing in a rough business like this?

A: Just lucky, I guess.

Q: Seriously, couldn't you be doing something more worth while? I understand you used to be a secretary.

A: What 'worth while'? Typing someone else's bullshit is worth while? Tell me about it.

Q: Yes. Well, what I mean is, why would you leave the status and security of an office job? This is men's work.

A: So? Maybe I just like men.

Q: Come on, now! A girl like you could find men *anywhere* she worked. Why don't you go back to being a secretary?

A: Why don't you go fuck your hat?

Q: Ha, ha. You're quite a joker, Chris.

A: That's me. A laugh a minute.

Q: You must have had some interesting experiences . . . a pretty girl, driving a taxi.

A: Well, sure. A few.

Q: Have you ever been stiffed or threatened?

A: No, not the way you probably mean it.

Q: Well, have you ever . . . has anyone ever . . .

A: Made a pass? Is that what you're trying to say?

Q: Ah, yes.

A: Are you kidding? I'm no Raquel Welch, but Jeezus!

Q: I guess you find that pretty obnoxious.

A: Tiresome would be a better word. Most of them slobber. But there've been one or two exceptions . . .

Q: Did any of these exceptions ever develop into anything?

A:

Q: I see. Well, you must have some experience that stands out. . . .

A: That's a cute way to put it.

Q: What do you mean?

A: Well, as it happens, I had this flasher in the car . . . just last week.

Q: And . . . ?

A: He had on this trench coat, just like flashers are supposed to have. He opened it and then unzipped his pants . . .

Q: What happened then?

A: He took his thing out and he started to . . . well, he started to beat off.

Q: Masturbate? Right in the car?

A: Say! You're real bright, aren't you?

Q: What did you do?

A: What the hell was I *supposed* to do? Scream?

Q: I mean, couldn't you have the dispatcher call the police, or something?

A: The police? You'll be all right!

Q: But surely that's what the police are for . . . to stop this kind
of . . .

A: Well, yeah. Provided they can get there in thirty seconds. How
long do you think it takes one of these sickies to . . .

Q: So you let it go.

A: No, not really. After I dropped him off, I got thinking maybe his
next show would be for some ten-year-old girl, and I wouldn't
want that. So I drove to the nearest police station.

Q: And what did the police do?

A: Oh, they wanted a description—height, build, age, if he had a
beard or whatever. . . .

Q: What did you tell them?

A: Almost nothing. I could hardly remember a goddam thing.

Q: But couldn't you tell the cops *anything?* How could you forget
what he looked like?

A: Well, you weren't there. And you're not a woman.

Q: Even so . . .

A: I did remember one thing. I was able to tell them that.

Q: What?

A: He wasn't circumcised.

 ACCOUNT PAYABLE

☛ "C'mon, Rosie! Get off the line . . . don't give me that shit, pal! Lemme talk to Marty . . ."

Even when you can hear only one side of them there are some conversations it's better not to hear at all. Al had told me a bit about the spot he was in—and from the way he'd jumped when the phone rang that night, it wasn't hard to figure out what the conversation was all about.

"Marty? . . . Yeah, it's Al. How ya doin', buddy? . . . Great, great. Yeah, I'm doin' fine too. . . . What? . . . Sure, I know. . . . Right. It screws up the book-keeping. But what the hell's the idea puttin' that big ape onto me? I thought you and me were friends. . . . What? . . . Yeah, I can take a joke. But that big sonofabitch is no joke. He'd break my back as quick as anybody's if you told him to. . . . No, I know you wouldn't. . . . Yeah . . . yeah, but no more of that stuff, huh? No friend of yours needs a call from Rosie. . . .

"What . . . ? No, I won't forget. Fifty next week for sure. . . . Sure, I can handle it. Fifty is just great. . . . No, not Rosie, I told you that ain't funny. . . . Right, Marty, a joke. So I'm laughin' my ass off. . . . Right, see you next week. G'night, ol' buddy."

Al dropped the phone into the cradle, leaned back with a sigh, and took a long pull from the bottle of beer at his elbow; there was a thin sheen of sweat on his forehead. He gave me a lop-sided grin that didn't quite come off.

"What the hell were we talkin' about when that damned phone rang, anyway?"

☞ Al told me about the time he'd borrowed the money from Marty:
"Why d'you want the money, Al?"

"Hell, Marty, it's that plate I'm renting . . . and I guess I got a little careless about the rent. Glickman's pushin' me, and I gotta spend a few hundred on the car . . ."

"Maybe you should go back to split sheets, like you were when you were drivin' for me. Better still, why don't you come back with me? I still got a couple of plates left after I sold the brokerage . . . and you were always square with me. I figured we always got along pretty good."

"Aw, you know I can't make any money that way, Marty . . . on split sheets . . ."

"It don't sound like you're doin' all that great, anyway . . . not when you're comin' to me for two grand!"

"Hell, I just got a little careless for a while, that's all. I can handle it. I just need a break."

"So you come to me, and I don't owe you 'hello' . . . but I've always liked you, goddammit. Which is why I don't want to lend you that kind of money."

"Is that supposed to make some kinda sense?"

"It should, Al, it should. How long've you been drivin' cab?"

"Oh, maybe six years . . ."

"And most of that you drove for me. So you *know* I ain't a bank . . . but you know I lend money. Right?"

"I heard. So I'm here."

"And you can't get it from a finance company, or maybe a rich uncle?"

"No way, Marty. I been through a coupla things . . ."

"Okay, okay. I don't want details, I just want you to know where it's all really at. I'll let you have the money, but I'll tell you straight, I wish it was almost anybody else but you. Because I don't want to see you in shit . . . and shit is where you'll be if you let me down. Like I said, I ain't a bank . . . and I don't sue nobody. I don't *have* to. Understand?''

"Yeah, Marty. I heard.''

"So it's the same for you as anybody else: six for five. You borrow five, you pay back six. So you'll owe me, let's see . . . twenty-four hundred. Two months.''

"Two months?''

"Right on, Al. If you can't handle it, forget you asked me.''

"I'll handle it . . . but the interest . . . Jesus!''

"Look. I'm givin' you a break, and I don't even want your business. I'd charge anybody else the same *vig* if it was only for a week. Just don't let me down. You don't need Rosie knockin' on your door.''

I guess not. I met Rosie once: huge, a Black Belt in whatever — and about as smart as a sack full of hammers. Something about his eyes lets you know he'd garrotte his own grandmother if Marty gave the word. But his job wasn't to kill; a thorough maiming was enough. Certain types of fractures can take a year to heal, and Rosie knew how to administer those.

☛ Now Al seemed to relax a bit. "Refill?'' I nodded. He swooped the empties from the table and came back with two fresh ones.

I said, "It's none of my business, but you gotta owe him a bundle by now.''

"A little over six big ones.''

"Christ! How long've you been letting it ride?''

"Well, I went about a year and a half there, at one point. But I been doin' better lately . . . ''

"I'd bloody well hope so! Have you got any idea what interest you're workin' on?''

"Sure. That's why I owe him six grand for two . . . after three years . . . and I already paid back more than half of the original two grand. Tell me about it.''

"Al, I don't know why the hell you're still alive! I don't know why Marty didn't put you in a fracture ward two years ago."

"Marty'd never lay a hand on me..."

"He doesn't have to. He's got Rosie."

"Come on! That bit with Rosie on the phone was a joke!"

"Sure it was. Why're you still sweating? Marty's trying to tell you something, and you'd better get your shit together."

"I still say Marty's my friend..."

"He must be, Al. You're still walking around, but I think you're out of your gourd. I may not know Marty as well as you do, but I drove for him for a while too... and I wouldn't tangle with that sonofabitch if I owned a cannon. This is *Mafia* stuff, baby!"

"Marty's not Mafia...!" Al slammed his bottle on the table. The ashtrays jumped about a foot. Al seemed startled by his own reaction. I said, "If he isn't, he's in as much shit as you are. Nobody gets to run a loan-shark scene as big as Marty's without at least making a deal with them. And if you've got to make a deal anyway, they own you."

"I don't believe it!"

"You just don't *want* to believe it. But think about it. The Family is full of loan sharks, right? It's all six-for-five... and they all have somebody like Rosie, right? So tell me what's the difference."

Al thought about if for a few seconds. I think it was a stall; I don't think I'd said a word he didn't already know... far better than I did. He smiled: "Maybe you're right. 'Nother brew?"

☞ Al finally made it—it took almost another two years—and he says Marty knocked off almost all of the *vig* for those two years, which I find a little hard to believe. But I guess it must've been true, or Al would *never* have climbed out of it.

Incidentally, Rosie managed to get himself blasted apart during those two years. If the cops know why, they're not talking; but I can't believe they don't know. It's a mean business.

And Al swears this:

On the day the final payment landed on Marty's desk, Al and his wife and kid were Marty's guests for dinner at the fanciest restaurant in town. Al says the bill was over two hundred dollars.

☞ "YOU'RE NEVER ALONE..."

☛ A lot of the downtown guys never turn on the two-way radio. Everyone to his own thing, I guess; but I can't imagine depending entirely on the street-corner trade for a living. For one thing, it can be a bit chancy if you give a damn about who (or what) climbs into the back seat. There are a few street corners in this town where a pick-up at two in the morning is unlikely to develop into a genteel exchange of views on baseball and the weather. There are a couple of corners, in fact, where you'd hesitate to pick up your own grandmother after dark.

Still, *somebody* has to handle the street trade; it's probably fifteen or twenty per cent of the taxi action in a city like this. We all play the streets from time to time—it would be stupid not to—but for my money, I'm happy to leave it to the guys who can't be bothered working the radio. There's little enough to keep your mind ticking over in this business, and nearly all of that is on the radio. So is all the fun.

☛ Phone rings in taxi office. Sweet young thing (order-taker) answers. Writes customer's address and destination on paper ticket about 3″ by 3″, time-stamps it, and passes it to the dispatcher.

And that's where the fun starts.

Dispatchers are an alien race. They all have at least two heads, and green, scaly tentacles; but by some trick of mass hypnosis they appear to us in almost human form. Their job, on a busy Friday rush-hour, is killing; the very best of them could make it big, any time, as stand-up comedians in Vegas. The dispatcher has no direct authority over the drivers, but it's a foolhardy driver who would defy him. There's a lot of difference between a forty-dollar shift and a hundred-dollar shift — and the dispatcher can easily make the difference.

The name of the dispatcher's game is to get rid of the orders as quickly as he can (by finding the car nearest to each order); the name of the driver's game is to avoid spending his life hauling groceries a distance of two blocks. It's a perpetual contest of wits— which the dispatcher always wins — and it can produce some interesting side-play. I guess the point I'm trying to make is that this constant fencing between the dispatcher and his drivers usually turns into a stream of chatter that must confuse the hell out of most passengers — and makes this whole, crazy business a bit of fun when we need it most. (And, dear Customer, you'll probably get your cab more quickly when we're having a few laughs. Believe it.)

☛ Like most drivers, I have a few favourite dispatchers who've made the years less of a drag than they might've been. In no particular order—and knowing damned well I'll miss a few of the best ones—I offer this short run-down of the ones I remember best:

I guess Donnie's the one who helped me survive that first, desperate week in the business—by refusing to let me keep making an ass of myself on the radio. ("And just *what* in God's name do you think you're doing *now*, Seven-eight? Smarten up, or I'll send you back to where you parked your camel!") Some people call Donnie the Old Man. He's not that old at all, but his awesome knowledge of every square inch of this town makes him one of the elders of the game.

"I sure hated to give you that tavern order, Seven-eight. I figured I'd lose you for the rest of the day."

"Not me, Donnie. I'm the stern, long-suffering type. This heat doesn't bother me."

"You mean you'd turn down something tall, cold, and full of gin?"

"Sir, I'll thank you to leave my wife out of this!"

☛ Tony was our intellectual: jazz buff, amateur astronomer, builder of model trains during the long, lonely midnight shifts. One of the really razor-edged dispatching minds in town — when he felt like it. Nobody could handle a frantic Friday rush-hour quite like Tony — when he felt like it.

"Make some time on that Muldrew order, Nine-oh. It's an emergency for the hospital."

"Right." (Squeal to a stop in front of house. Living-room drapes are open. Watch mother carefully and slowly brushing hair of twelve-year-old daughter; they know you're there. Mother and daughter finally stroll out to car. Break maybe twenty laws in rush to hospital. Kid is obvious whiner, but no signs of desperate emergency.)

Later: "How'd you make out with that hospital rush, Nine-oh? Everything okay?"

"Hah! Some emergency!"

"How's that?"

"Well . . . let me put it this way: I think, if I were engaged in the practice of medicine . . . I would've prescribed an enema."

☛ I don't know how Hippie John got his name; it's all buried somewhere in the mythology of another taxi company. I once heard him described as "a big guy with a kind of washed-out Afro — but he's white". An excellent drinking companion; and (apparently) a swordsman of some note.

For reasons there'd be no point in trying to remember, Hippie John and I used to crack at each other in phony Cherman Agzents: "Vass ist das, Sieben-eight? You *rr*efuse to disclose your vhereabouts? V*err*y interesting . . ."

"Nein, Herr Unterfuehrer... das ist ein vershtunken traffic jam.... Ich bin gestuck hier."

"Das ist nicht excuse, Sieben-eight. Du bist ein Scheisskopf, undt you vill present yourself at Schutzstaffel Headqvarters for interrogation. Undt you vill bring your papers, please..."

Childish? Certainly. But it makes the day go a hell of a lot faster.

A good dispatcher is a lot more interesting than a drunk—or a fat lady going two blocks to her doctor's for reducing pills. The downtown guys, with their paranoia and their racetrack mentality and dirty cars—and with their radios shut off—miss all the fun. It must be a hell of a way to make a living.

One of my fares said it best:

It was that quiet, almost-mystical time — about three in the morning—when the radio would be silent except for some of the clowning around. She listened, puzzled, to some of the chatter. (It takes a while to tune your ears to a VHF radio.) Then she laughed; a great, roaring, whooping belly-laugh you seldom hear from a woman.

"Did you hear that?" she asked, after she'd calmed down a bit.

I guess I hadn't really been listening. I said, "No, I missed it. What was it?"

"Oh, I can't tell you if you missed it. But do they always talk crazy like that?"

"Well... sometimes. I guess we all get a bit slap-happy, this time of night...."

"You must like your work. I bet you like your work."

"Sure." I thought about it some more. "Yeah, most of the time I really do. Why?"

"Don't you know? Don't you know what you've got going for you, even at three in the morning?"

"No. What?"

She looked at me. "You're never alone." She pointed at the radio. "You're just never alone..."

 LAW 'N' ORDER

☛ I guess almost everybody has heard the old one about the bank robber who tried to hail a cab for his get-away — and learned that you can never get a taxi in the rain.

This story is about a bank robber who should've walked!

Saturday is a good day to make money — provided you don't mind listening to big chunks of your sanity breaking off and falling away. That greatest of folklore villains, the Timid Sunday Driver, has been overtaken in his supreme villainy by the White-Knuckled Saturday Idiot; and the family station-wagon has become an instrument of pure terror. Obviously ten minutes a week of driving practice — to and from the supermarket — just isn't enough for Mother to learn on. (Sometimes Father drives on Saturday, and you have to wonder if he parked his brain under a rock for the weekend.)

This Saturday my fare was nagging absently at me as I eased the car through the mob of shoppers chugging about the big parking lot like an ant colony gone mad. I don't think she was listening to the nagging any more than I was. The cab directly in front of us stopped suddenly, and the voice from the back seat rose to a whine.

I didn't recognize the plate number on the other cab; the driver had stopped to let some nut extricate his car from the stunningly impossible position he'd gotten himself into. And I didn't take much notice of the guy who came out of the bank at that moment and climbed into the other taxi.

137

Within seconds we were moving again; the monologue from the back seat became a muttering, probably habitual. By the time I'd reached a point fifty feet past the doors of the bank, the other cab had turned into the "out" lane and I couldn't see it. As I was about to make my turn I glanced in the rear-view mirror—I do that a lot on Saturdays, a kind of nervous tic — and saw the kefuffle in front of the bank. Half a dozen people had burst out the doors and begun running all over the parking lot; I thought I recognized the manager and a couple of the tellers. "What now?" I wondered. "Somebody heist the place?" It wasn't any of my business; I had a fare and a car full of groceries.

She wasn't going far. Within three or four minutes I had her home and the goodies unloaded. Just as I climbed back behind the wheel the dispatcher, sounding puzzled, cracked: "Anybody just pick up a fare from the Eastown Plaza? Like, five minutes ago?"

I picked up the mike. "Yeah. Seven-eight. I got one."

"Where'd it go, Seven-eight?"

"Glensheppard. The one you gave me . . . groceries." I still wasn't thinking about the excitement at the bank.

"Oh, yeah, right. Okay, anyone else pick one up at the Eastown? I got the police on the phone."

No answer.

"Come *on*, guys! I know *somebody* got a fare at the bank. Now, who was it?"

Then I remembered what was wrong with the fare I'd seen climbing into the cab ahead of me at the plaza: you don't often see a guy in torn jeans, sneakers, and a mackinaw shirt—and carrying a black attaché case out of a bank.

It hit me that this wasn't a very good time for the dispatcher to make an issue of it: what if the guy was still in the other cab? Hell, five minutes after the robbery he'd *have* to be—and he could hear the radio, too. One thing you don't need in the car is a thief who knows he's cornered. I started to sweat for the other driver. I was

about to say something over the radio, then decided that nothing I
could say would help. Maybe the damage had already been done.

Suddenly, a young voice I didn't recognize: "Hey! I just dropped
a fare a minute ago. I didn't see what store he came out of...
but I got 'im at the Eastown..."

"You dropped him already? What's your number, son?" The
dispatcher sounded relieved—as he damned well should be.

"I'm drivin' car Nine. What's it all about, anyway?"

"Where're you now?"

"I was just headin' back to the Twenty post..."

"Just a minute, car Nine..." The air went dead for a few
seconds, then: "Okay, Nine. You go back to the post and hang in
there. The police'll be there in a minute."

"Cops? I don't want no cops! What in hell's it all about?"

"It's all right, son . . . and watch your language on the radio. The
police just want to ask you about your fare."

"You mean the guy from the Eastown? He's drinkin' beer at the
Knobby right now. He wanted me to come in and have one with
him. . . ."

(The Knobby is a big tavern with an interesting reputation—and
it's about a half-mile from the scene of the robbery.)

The cops had the loser before he'd finished his second beer;
jeans, attaché case, and all. The whole exercise took maybe seven
minutes. It's a hell of a way to rob a bank.

☛ CONTRIBUTOR'S CORNER

☛ Most of the guys in the fleet knew I was getting a book together, and I don't recall anyone objecting to being a part of it. Crazy Charlie, for one, went a bit farther and offered a typed outline of one of his experiences.

Apart from a couple of deletions — solely for the purpose of eliminating meaningless numbers that would serve only to confuse things — here is Charlie's account, exactly as he gave it to me:

AS I WAS IN THE_____AREA, THIRD UP WHEN I SAID NO WAY WILL I BE HERE ALL NIGHT, SO I MOVED FROM THE *** TO THE***. AS I WAS SITTING THERE OR SLEEPING I DON'T REALY KNOW, A CALL CAME TO ME: CAR ELEVEN ARE YOU STILL IN THE *** AREA SO I SAID ROGER, REFUSING A PICKUP TO THE TRAIN THINKING THAT THE CALL WAS GOING FARTHER SO. // THE DISPATCHER SAID CHARLIE THIS MUST BE YOUR LUCKY DAY. GET 90 MORNELLE APARTMENT *** GOING TO THE BEER STORE AND RETURN, WELL I COUD TELL BY HIS LAUGH THERE WAS SOMETHING SO. // I WENT TO SEE AND WHEN ### I WRANG THE BUZZER, A VOICE FROM INSIDE SAID HANG ON I'M NOT SO DAM DEAF. SO I WENT AND SAT IN THE CAB TO WAIT, WHEN TO MY SURPRIZE CAME THIS BIG FAT LADY AND HER RETARD SON.

SHE HAD ON A OLD BLUE DRESS THAT HAD NOT BEN WASHED SINCE NEW SHE HAD FOOD ALL OVER THE FRONT OF IT AND BIG

SWEAT STAINS UNDER HER ARMS. AND SHE ROLLED DOWN THE
WINDOW AND WAS SHOUTING TO ALL OUR NIGRO FRIENDS
CHOICE WORDS. THEN SHE SAID TO ME YOU CAB DRIVERS ARE ALL
DIRTY FREAKS.

GOD DAM FREAKS. WELL I DID /T MIND THE INSULTS BUT BY
THE TIME SHE GOT OUT OF MY CAB THE STINK WAS SO BAD THAT.
IROLLED DOWN THE WINDOWS THINKING THAT WOULD HELP.
BUT THE STINK WAS SO BAD I HAD TO BY A CAN OF LYSOL
DEODERENT SPRAY THAT COST ME $1/50 AND THE FARE WAS 1.60
SO MY FRIENDS IT GOES TO SHOW WHAT A MAN /// GO THROUGH
TO MAKE A GOD DAM DIME.

TO ALL MY CAB FRIENDS

BIG DEAL

CHARLIE.

Charlie's experience was scarcely unique; most of us have had
the same fare at one time or another. But Charlie's eloquence
seemed more appropriate than the standard biological expletives
most of us have directed at the lady in question.

I guess we lack Charlie's literary talent.

☞ YOU WIN ONE WHEN YOU CAN

☞ It is often suggested that many of Kenny's best stories lean more toward fantasy than truth; a kind of Apocrypha of the taxi scriptures, if you like. Maybe this is so, but I don't see that it matters a hell of a lot. Anyone who insists upon literal truth has built himself a problem with which I won't concern myself — any more than Kenny would.

If you were to meet Kenny you might say to yourself, "Hah! *This* guy has no business driving hack — obviously, he's just putting in time until his nerves heal, or whatever." If you're *really* a student of people you'll say, "He belongs behind a desk, a big one. Hell, maybe he *owns* this outfit...."

You'd be wrong on all counts, but your guesses could've been worse. Kenny's not hiding from his nerves any more (if he ever did), but he knows a thing or two about big desks; and he *did* own a taxi company—but not this one. The fact is that he may be one of the few cab-drivers in town who's developed his own sense of the absurd to the point where he can be happy with the job. While the rest of us bitch about the money, the drunks, the arrogance of some of our fares, the drunks, the Inspection Office—and the drunks— Kenny just goes about his business, collecting stories to share with us over a beer.

☞ It's when he passes within a mile of a speed-trap that Kenny becomes a source of legend. Everybody in this business gets tickets now and then; you just can't drive a thousand miles a week in city traffic without committing the occasional sin. Breaks of the game. But I'm damned if Kenny isn't the only guy I *ever* heard of who's been busted for speeding by: (1) an airplane, (2) a paddy wagon, and (3) a horse.

Before we get into that, it must be said that Kenny is a solid citizen; a worker; law-and-order. Solid. It's just that he doesn't like traffic cops. (Hell, neither do *other* cops.) He got his revenge one time, though:

"I guess it was about five o'clock on a Sunday morning . . . the sun was just coming up, anyway . . . there's just nothin' on the streets.

"Suddenly I spot this green Plymouth about a quarter-mile up the road, right on the edge of the Esso station. It's gotta be radar, even though this is a pretty dumb time for it. Like I said, there's just nothin' moving. I've been doing about fifty, but I think I've spotted him in time. I'm down to maybe thirty when I pass him, and the sonofabitch is sound asleep! I figure: why not? This is too good to miss!

"I pick up the mike. 'Don, there's a police officer unconscious in his car, up here at the Esso station.' I give Don the address. 'He might be hurt. Maybe you'd better call the cop shop.' Don is no dummy, and he knows I'd stop and check it out if I thought there was anything really wrong. After a minute: 'They've got it, Ken. You goin' to stick around there?' I tell him I'm not. 'I didn't think so,' Don says. I almost wish I *had* stuck around to watch the fun."

Why is that?

"Look. There's no one in deeper shit than a cop who falls asleep on duty. And a radar cop? Beautiful! I hope they sent a sergeant to check it out!"

Rough? Maybe. But read on.

☞ The paddy-wagon story is interesting:

(For those whose generation may not recognize the term, a paddy wagon is one of those big, barred vans the police use to transport big bunches of suspects, like when they raid a whore-house or a dope-ring. Or a card game. "Black Maria" means the same thing—even though they're yellow in this town.)

Now, a cop on paddy-wagon duty isn't going to be much in-terested in traffic; he'll leave that to the boys on the quota system. For one thing, there's no radar in a paddy wagon, probably not even a traffic-ticket book; besides, he has his hands full with the drunks and whores and bookies in the back of the bus. Right?

Maybe not. Kenny got nailed for seven miles over, in a thirty-mile zone—by a cop who jumped out of a Black Maria. He swears it. (I happen to believe him, by the way. Nothing has ever con-vinced me that life is a logical process.)

☛ And then there was the airplane:

Most people don't know this, but the provincial police force in these parts began as a kind of air force. They had more planes than cars, and their biggest job was to discourage the smuggling of booze across the border during Prohibition. (It was legal to make booze and sell it—it was almost a capital offence to buy it or drink it; and running it across the Detroit River or Lake Ontario by fast boat was an offence that could easily get you shot on sight. Still, there were a hell of a lot of fast boats around, and more than one fine political fortune began on the water. Prohibition is the best thing that ever happened to some of the big money around here.)

The air force is still with us: smaller, newer, and vastly outnum-bered by black-and-white cruisers. You've seen those signs on some of the main highways: Patrolled By Aircraft. Believe it. Kenny does.

I've often wondered how it works. Kenny explained:

"They can't spot licence numbers from the air, but they can usually spot the make of the car, and they can sure as hell tell the colour. So what they do is radio down to the next cruiser and have him stop a whole line of traffic. The cruiser cop gets out of the car with a walkie-talkie while the plane circles at a couple hundred feet: 'Back a bit, Harry. No, over in the outside lane. That's it. Now, a bit forward. A couple more cars. See the green Cougar, Harry? That's the one! I make it twelve miles over.' "

Guess who owns the only green Cougar within fifty miles?

Kenny told me something else that's interesting: the cruiser cop writes out the ticket, but the cop in the plane is the one who lays the charge. He's the one you meet in court — and you've never even seen the sonofabitch.

It makes a guy wonder.

☛ Of course most of us don't bother going to court over speeding tickets; the day off work usually costs more than the fine. I'm sure the bastards count on that. I'll bet Kenny wishes he'd gone to court on the horse caper, though.

It seems to me that a cop on horseback gives himself a bit of a handicap as a speed-trap — when he sets himself up to do business in a forty-mile zone. Assuming he has some means of clocking you in heavy traffic (doubtful enough) — how the hell does he *catch* you?

This one caught Kenny, and I guess it really doesn't matter *how*. The blue ticket is what matters: five miles over the limit, which would be a cheesy enough rap if it was handed out by the angel Gabriel himself. Kenny was jumping mad when he told us. But, as always, he had to lay that one extra little bit of knowledge on us:

Mounted cops never get off their horses while they're writing out tickets. (I'm almost ashamed to say I've never noticed that.) What a mounted cop will do, says Kenny, is position his horse so that it faces away from your car at an angle. This makes it more visible to oncoming traffic. It also places the horse's ass right at your window, maybe a bit inside it.

Now, the police in this town have some splendid animals: most are chestnuts, glossy, beautifully groomed, noble — and not one of the god-damned things is house-broken. The thing to do is watch the tail. The slightest raising of the tail ...

You may never have a horse's ass jammed against your open car window; you will probably never be busted by Sky King in his god-damned Cessna aircraft, either. But — unless you're totally blind, or sufficiently wired in to the Establishment that life wears a different face for you than it does for most of us — you know that horseshit can drop from just about anywhere. It's just a question of how high the piles get before they begin to bother you.

Kenny doesn't like to see the piles get too high. His revenge against the sleeping radar cop, on that quiet Sunday morning, may have contained the flaw of excess. But who's to say? How high do you have to let the horseshit get? Hell, you win one when you can.

☞ THE HOMECOMING

☛ It's funny how people always come home without warning—after months, maybe a year or so—and nobody knows how to act.

Sam and Dave and I had been arguing about hockey or something, and we didn't notice Joe until he pulled out a chair and sat down at our table. "Joe! Joe Harris, for chrissake! How you been, guy? Must be at least a year..."

"Three. Three years yesterday."

"Yeah? That long? Well, dammit... good to see you. Time really flies, huh?"

Joe smiled: a thin, knowing kind of smile. He didn't say anything.

Dave cleared his throat and said, "I guess that was a dumb way to put it. But hell, you know what I mean." If Joe knew what he meant, he sure wasn't about to bail him out; he just kept smiling that thin smile. The silence got pretty heavy for a minute. I guess we were all thinking the same thing: Time depends on a lot of things, including which side of the wall you happen to be on.

Joe had always been an easy guy to get along with, although there was a dark side to him that none of the rest of us really understood. He'd taken the fall on a rap that really shouldn't have cost him more than a year's probation—a little thing involving a bit too much grass—but he'd lucked onto a judge who happened to be running something of a crusade at the time.

149

We were all a little shocked when it happened, and there wasn't a damned thing we could do to help him. Maybe that laid a guilt trip on us; I don't know. Still, I'd always figured if anyone could do those three years standing on his head, Joe would be that guy.

He caught me studying him, and the smile got just a bit tighter. He looked about the same, maybe ten pounds lighter and a little more than three years older. And the eyes, something about the eyes. You wouldn't notice if you hadn't known him pretty well. Jessie came over to take our order. I guess she'd never seen Joe before, and I could almost hear her wondering. Jessie could turn granite to soup, but she didn't try any of that on Joe.

He looked at our nearly empty beer mugs. "The same again for my friends, and a triple rye and water for me." Jessie hesitated a half-second too long, looking at Sam and Dave and me with some kind of question in her eyes. Joe's voice was almost a whisper, but it cracked like a whip: "Now, sweetheart, not later. *Move!*" Nobody five feet from the table would've heard him.

I'd never seen Jessie really rattled before. She stood at the service bar, waiting for our order, and watching Joe in just about the way she would've watched a snake. I said, "Joe, don't be rough on Jessie. She's good people."

He turned toward the bar; she made a point of looking the other way. He tilted his chair back and laughed. "Yeah," he said, "she's a good-lookin' broad, all right." He hooked his thumbs in his belt, grinning. "Broads. Haven't seen many in the last little while. Maybe I should try my luck with this one." He winked in my direction.

I said, "Oh, I don't think so, Joe. Not with this one."

His eyebrows shot up. "You got a claim staked, or what?"

"Hell, no. I'm just a father-image. And she's married."

"That makes a difference?"

"With Jessie, yes. I think it just might."

Joe reared back in the chair and laughed again. "Relax. I was just tryin' to see if you'd maybe cornered the market."

A nice dig. So, the good old taxi-land telegraph had found him—even up there. He'd know I'd been seeing Laura once in a while, and the stories would be mightily embellished. I tried a smile; it felt as if it had been stapled on. I said, "Hell, no. I quit trying to look after all of them years ago. . . . No more stamina, I guess."

"Bullshit. I was hoping there'd be less of it when I got out. You owe me something better than that, old buddy."

Jessie brought our drinks and banged them down in front of us without comment. She hurried back to the kitchen as if to get the hell out of our sight for a minute. The heavy silence came back, then Sam and Dave both started to talk at once: "Where you stayin', Joe?" and, "You comin' back to driving cab, or what?" Joe fielded their questions without really answering them; finally they called for their bills and left, I'd guess a good hour before they'd planned to.

Joe's eyes darted about the room, looking anywhere but at me. I watched him, trying to figure how much brutalizing three years on the Inside can do to a man. Some, apparently: there was a cynical edge and a tension I'd never seen in him before, and there was no humour behind those quick eyes. I wondered how Laura was taking it—his kids wouldn't know him at all.

About Laura: We really had it on for a couple of years; living together when the vibes were right, avoiding each other when they weren't. She alternated between being a head-case, and maybe the wisest woman I've ever known. We never could get it right.

Joe knew all of this before he married Laura. I think he even knew that one of her kids could very easily have been mine. Much of what I'd felt about her involved charging about on a white horse; but God, she was a beautiful woman! I think I must've fallen into those utterly astounding brown-black eyes a thousand times. Still, I was vaguely relieved when it was all over and Joe married her. Hell, she'll always be special; no point in kidding myself. Joe knows that, too, I think.

His wolfish grin came back. "I ain't been home yet, old buddy.

Is there anything I should know?"

"You mean you haven't seen Laura and the kids yet? Why the hell not?"

"Oh, let's just say I wanted to check out a couple things first . . . like what *you've* been doing for kicks lately. Stuff like that."

"You sure you want to talk about it here? I got a few beers at my place . . ."

"No. Right here is fine."

"Okay, Joe. Let's have it. What's on your mind?" I hoped to hell my voice sounded better than I felt.

"I been hearin' things. I don't like what I hear."

"Up there? Is that where you been hearing them?"

"Sure. Where else?"

"That's just great. You hear a lot of shit from some con you don't even know . . ."

"Oh, I knew him. So would you."

"And he told you I been screwin' around with Laura."

"Did I say that?"

"Never mind what you said. Is that what you think?"

Joe seemed to shrink a bit, looking into his drink. I tried to remember when we'd been friends. We hadn't, really; he'd just happened along when Laura was ready to settle down. And Joe and I had ridden along on that strange, unlikely kind of respect that happens between two guys who have known the same woman. Finally he looked up at me, and I couldn't read his eyes at all. "You been seeing her, haven't you?"

I thought: Shit! There's no way to make this sound right to a man who got out of the can yesterday. I said, "Okay, Joe. I'll tell you how it's been. I'll tell you just one time, and you can believe it or stuff it. You might try asking Laura, too. She doesn't lie, and you goddam well know it.

"Yeah, I've been seeing her. You're in the can and she's on welfare . . . so she and the kids get to eat steak maybe twice a year. I brought them all up here for dinner a few times, and I got the kids some stuff for Christmas. That's it, and that's *all*!"

"Beautiful story, old buddy. Wait'll I get my violin."

"Joe, I don't give a shit whether you believe it or not. Actually, I *do* give a shit . . . for Laura's sake."

"Yeah. Well, I got to believe what I hear. . . . "

"Look, Joe. What Laura and I had going was five, six years ago. We never kidded you about that. Go see her."

"I don't have to. She'll be here."

"Here? You called her?"

"No, but she'll be here. From what I hear, she's here every night : . . maybe doin' a bit of hooking, too."

"That's complete bullshit! She's in here maybe twice a month. And hooking? Christ! You know her better than that! She'll hardly let anyone buy her a drink. Even me."

"Even you. How chummy!"

"Oh for godsake, Joe! You want it written in blood?"

"No, I don't need nothin' in writing. I'll find out." He lifted a corner of the tablecloth to show me the .38 Smith & Wesson sitting in his lap. "And it ain't just you. But I'll find out. She'll be here."

I've seen lots of guns; hell, I was a weapons instructor in the army. I've been shot at and missed and shit at and hit more than most — but I managed to work up a cold sweat at the sight of that revolver under the table. This was not the Joe I'd known for years, and there just wasn't a goddam thing left to talk about. (I thought up all kinds of schemes to get the gun away from him, or to somehow warn Laura, but nothing that had a hope in hell of working. A .38 is a mean instrument, and its purpose is rather specific.)

So, we waited.

Jessie brought Joe a couple more triples; at his insistence, I worked my way through a couple more beers. I didn't bother trying to suggest that it was time for me to get back to work. Laura didn't show; there just wasn't any reason why she would. Finally, about a half-hour after Jim closed the bar, Joe called for the bill and left.

As soon as he'd gone, I phoned Laura's number two or three times, but the line was busy. She often leaves it off the hook when she doesn't want to be bothered.

I thought about calling the cops, but a "domestic" is not the kind of news they want to hear. Her place was only a couple of blocks away, and Joe would almost certainly be there before the cops were. I thought of driving to Laura's, then remembered why the police try to avoid this kind of thing. It could only be worse if Joe walked in with me already there.

And I had a good, strong hunch that he'd never use the gun—even three years in the drum couldn't change him *that* much. He was more scared than furious, anyway; I counted on it. Nobody, but *nobody*, comes out a hero in a man-wife scuffle, so I sweated the next several hours.

My hunch was a good one: Joe never used the gun. In fact he never showed up at Laura's at all. He could be dead for all anybody knows.

Laura? I see her once in a while, but we make a point of keeping everything on an old-friends basis. Platonic? You've got to prove platonic to me; nobody with serviceable glands buys any of that. But we try, we really do. She tells me things about Joe, things that only a wife could know, things that aren't very pleasant to hear. (You have to be careful what you believe—women like Laura know a few of the angles.) But she's still beautiful, dammit.

And I like her kids, especially the oldest one. He reminds me of someone I should know, like in an old, old photograph. I'd never ask Laura, though — not yet. And I have no old photographs of my own.

# FALSE START

☞ My fare was just getting out of the car when Don came up the hospital driveway. Fast. Through my passenger's steady stream of chatter I'd heard Don say something about "heart attack" and "police". He flashed his lights and gave a short blast on the horn as he pulled up right behind me; I piled out of my car to see what was happening.

We were trying to wrestle two hundred pounds of dead weight out of Don's car when the cruiser came wheeling in.

As the three of us carried the guy through the Emergency doors, I had a flash of a scene from the movie they made around one of Hemingway's good ones: *A Farewell to Arms*; the scene where they moved in for a close-up of Jennifer Jones, just as she died. She looked up at the hero, deep into his eyes — and said, "You bastard!" Then it seemed as if they slipped a grey filter over the camera lens.

The colour drains right out of them when the heart quits.

The cop followed the stretcher down the hall, talking to the intern. Don and I felt pretty superfluous, so we walked back out to his cab. I lit a couple of smokes, handed him one, and wondered why my hands were shaking worse than his. After all, *he'd* watched the guy die—*I* hadn't.

For some reason I don't remember just now, I got into Don's car while he moved it to an out-of-the-way corner: the stench was awful. When they die, all the sphincters let go; the bladder and bowels have no further reason to hold their contents. The poor bastard's clothing had contained the worst of the mess, and we did what we could to clean up the rest of it.

"Think he'll make it?" I asked, mostly for something to break the silence.

Don snorted. "Nahh! When they let go like that, they're finished."

"Yeah. I guess so." The smell was still pretty stong; I rolled the window down. "But, Jesus! He was so damned *white* . . ."

"Poor bastard. He didn't seem too bad when he got in the car." Don flicked his cigarette out the window. "Y'know . . . the last thing he said, he wanted me to stop and get him something to read . . . in case he had to stay in overnight."

"Shit. He suffer much?"

"Well . . . not long, anyway. We were talking, then he let out a kind of grunt and grabbed my arm. I guess it hurt like hell . . . his face was real twisted . . . but it was all over in four, five seconds."

"He grabbed your arm?"

"Yeah, and I goddam near went off the road. Scared the hell out of me. . . ."

Don's voice trailed off. He lit another cigarette—on the filter end —and butted it in the ashtray, looking disgusted. "Where the hell's that cop?"

"I guess we have to wait for him . . ."

"Well, *I* do, for sure. Maybe you're a witness, too."

We waited a few minutes, not saying much.

"Hell, I'm going back in there," Don said, his patience gone.

With that, the cop came out through the Emergency doors, looking everywhere but in our direction. Don intercepted him halfway to the cruiser. "Hey! What's happening?"

"What?" The cop seemed preoccupied. "Oh, yeah. Well, he's gone."

"Gone?"

"Yeah. Dead."

"It took all this time to figure that out? Christ, I could've told them that a half-hour ago . . . "

"I don't know what you're talking about," the cop said. "He just died a couple of minutes ago."

"Aw, come on!" Don was almost shouting. "He was deader'n a whore's conscience when I brought him in here!"

"Wrong. They opened him up and got him started again. Three times. The last time, he kept going almost ten minutes."

"They cranked him up *three times*? That poor son of a bitch! Why couldn't they just let him go?"

The cop looked at Don. Hard.

"Buddy, don't knock it. This way, he died in the hospital. Officially. Right?"

"If you say so."

"I say so. They did you a hell of a favour."

"A favour? Me?"

"Sure. Tell me, how many forms do you think you would've had to fill out if he'd died in your cab . . . officially, that is?"

"Holy shit! I guess you're right. . . . " Don seemed awed.

The cop smiled, waved a casual salute, and ambled toward the cruiser. His night was just beginning.

# PSYCHO WARD

☛ If the world ever had a sudden attack of sanity, there'd be a lot of cabs sitting around empty.

There's just no way to guess what in hell will be going on in the back seat ten seconds after you pick up your fare. Of course, it's pretty tame most of the time; nothing more remarkable than a sixtyish, fur-bearing woman on her way to the doctor's — in a girdle so tight you can almost hear her ears ringing. Or perhaps some good-natured drunk who has decided that you have plenty of time to hear his life story.

And then there are the other times . . .

Like the night the fire extinguisher went off in Big John's car. It seems he'd picked up this nut at one of the local pubs, right around closing. (Fun time. The people who close the joints are often the ones who opened them—thirteen hours earlier.) I'd better let Big John tell it:

"He's not all that hammered, y'know? Oh, he's had a few, but still tracking pretty good. Anyway, he wants me to take him to this small apartment building just around the corner and wait a couple minutes. Something he has to pick up. From where I'm parked I can see the whole goddam thing . . . what he picks up is a great, bloody fire extinguisher . . . rips it right off the wall in the lobby. Then he hustles it out to the car and shoves it in the back seat."

Big John makes a chain of overlapping rings on the table with the bottom of his beer mug. Thinking.

Then: "Shit, it's none of my business... I can't spend half my time reporting these clowns to the cops... so I start to drive him home. I guess it was home. A good run, anyway. We get to talking... and I don't say nothin' about the fire extinguisher. All of a sudden there's this stink that would knock a buzzard off a shit-wagon, and a funny kind of hissing comin' from the back. I wheel over to the side of the road and stop, and we both look over the back of the seat at the god-damnedest mess you ever seen.

"You know what? This asshole has laid the bloody thing on its side... and it's the kind of extinguisher that goes off when the stuff inside gets tipped over and starts to mix. I guess it could've been worse... when you turn 'em all the way over they *really* go!"

Big John takes a big swallow of his beer; Liz comes over to see if we're ready for another round. A couple of the guys order dinner, so it's a minute or two before Big John continues:

"You would not believe the crud that spews out of that goddam thing... foam, gas, a pissy-looking fluid... and the stink! Jesus! Think we can shut that mother off? I even try tying a knot in the hose. Then we finally get smart and heave the sonofabitch out on the road.

"It's funnier'n hell when I think back on it... but how'm I gonna get all that shit out of my car? By this time the foam is damn near up to the roof! I say, 'Buddy, that's gotta cost you. I'm out of business till I clean up this fuckin' mess....'

"'Sure,' he says. 'Is twenty enough?'

"That shook me. I was all ready to thump him one... most of 'em figure they can crap in your pocket, as long as the meter's running. What can I say? He paid the fare on top of it, too."

Nobody said anything for a moment. Then, "You get the mess cleaned up all right, John?"

"Oh, yeah. It wasn't as bad as it looked. But I still got some of that stink in the car. I tried everything..."

Someone asked, "What the hell was he tryin' to prove... rippin' the thing off the wall like that? You said he wasn't that drunk."

"That's right. I asked him why he stole a fire extinguisher in the first place, for chrissake."

"What'd he say?"

"He said, 'Oh, hell, I dunno . . . I guess I just always wanted one.'"

☛ You don't believe all this stuff about the full moon, do you . . . about how it makes a lot of people go ape for two or three days every month? Of course not. It's just not scientific. An old wives' tale.

But you might want to try an experiment—a slightly expensive one, maybe—purely in the interest of science:

Have a party on the night of the next full moon. Lay on plenty of booze and games to keep everyone busy; the more competitive the games, the better. Invite a lot of people, people you've known for years, whose behaviour is absolutely predictable. Then sit back and watch. Carefully.

It's possible that none of the following will happen, but don't bet the mortgage money on it.

Harry loves animals, and they know it. When he was a kid he used to bring home injured worms and nurse them back to health. Harry is probably the kindest, most decent man you know. Some time during the evening he will kick your cat, viciously.

Every group has its Ideal Couple: Carol is blonde, soft, adoring; Joe is tall, witty, and attentive to her every whim. They were made for each other—everybody knows that. But a game of charades or bridge may get a little out of hand this evening, and Carol will say something to Joe that is utterly unforgivable; and Joe just might reward her with a good rap on the mouth.

So much for your party. Sorry. So much for old wives' tales.

Cops know all about the time of the full moon.

Item: A young mother stuffs her two-year-old into a linen closet, touches a match to the sheets — and locks the door. All the neighbours say she was an ideal mother. The father says her life revolved around the child.

Item: A man of sixty-five, known among a wide circle of friends as a guy without a mean bone in his body, shoots his wife of forty years. The police count seven bullet-wounds—and can't come up with the slightest hint of a motive.

The police have their own way of handling the full-moon times. Officially, it's business as usual—but ask any cop, privately. There are just a few more cruisers on the road, and the emergency squads are a little bit readier. A cop explained it to me once: "Look. *You* know it happens. *We* know it happens. But there're enough marginal nuts around . . . we're not going to give them an excuse to go over the edge . . . by admitting that the full moon means anything special to us. You dig?"

I dig.

Cab drivers dread the full moon, too—especially when it comes on a Friday or Saturday night. Or on the day the welfare cheques arrive. With luck, you'll never have to spend any time in a taxi office. If you do, especially around full-moon times, you might hear something like this:

(Phone rings.)

"Taxi."

"Hello. Hello. Is this the taxi?"

"Yes, this the taxi. Where are you?"

"I'm at the store. The grocery store."

"Yes, ma'am, but where are you?"

"The grocery store. I *always* shop here."

"Yes, I know. But which grocery store?"

"Oh, *you* know. I take a cab every week . . ."

"Well, ma'am, I'd like to help you, but I have to know exactly where you are . . ."

"Well, I never! I'm your best customer, and you won't send me a taxi . . ."

(Line goes dead.)

Or:

"Taxi."

"Hey, baby! Who's dispatching?"

"Where are you, sir?"

"Nev' mind that shit. Who's on the board?"

"Who's calling?"

"Jerry. Tell that sumbitch it's Jerry . . . ol' buddy Jerry."

"I'll tell him, sir . . . just a minute . . . "

(A moment passes.)

"Sir? The dispatcher says he doesn't know any Jerry. But if you want to call him on the other line . . . the number is . . . "

"The hell with that noise, sister. You just tell him I want a car here, and I want it *now*! An' tell the driver he's gonna cash a cheque for me . . . "

"I'll see what I can do, sir. Where are you?"

"Lissen, baby, I don' need this shit. Just send me a fuckin' cab, okay?"

(He hangs up.)

And so it goes. It can be a long, long night.

☛ The kid was maybe eighteen, and he thought They were after him. He was shaking when he climbed into the car. "You got a gun?"

I figured he was kidding. "Hell, no," I said. "I don't even have a pencil. Somebody stole it. What's the problem?"

"The last cab-driver, the one that dropped me here . . . *he* had a gun. He was gonna kill me!"

"Aw, come on, son! Why would he want to kill you? Did you know him?"

"No. But they're *all* after me! All of them . . . "

"All of who? Who's after you?"

"I don't know, but they're gonna get me!" He rambled on about something I couldn't quite catch, then: "I don't want to die! I haven't done anything!" His breath started to come in great, wracking sobs; and I swear I could hear his teeth chattering. I eased out of the traffic and stopped the car.

I turned to look at him: he was curled, huddled, cowering in the far corner of the back seat, still sobbing. It struck me that I had never seen anyone cower before, not really. It isn't good to see.

I've never believed in midnight psychiatry. It can be messy enough when it's only some chick trying to use you, to get back at her man for some imagined affront — and God knows you get plenty of those when you work nights—but it can be a whole hell of a lot messier when you try to play head games with a fare. Like the kid who was still sobbing and mumbling in the back seat of my car.

"Hey, son. Come on, now . . . get a hold of yourself." I tried to reassure him with a couple of good claps on the shoulder. "Snap out of it! Come on, now!"

"But I don't want to die!" He shrank further into the corner and stared at me, eyes wide.

"You're not going to die. Tell you what. There's a police station just a couple of blocks away. Let's go in and talk to them, okay?"

"No! Not the police . . . "

"Sure! You got a problem like this, you go to the cops. Every time." I tried to keep my voice friendly and encouraging.

"You think so? You think it's safe?"

"Safe as churches. Let's go."

It wasn't until we stood side by side at the counter in the cop shop that I realized how big the kid was: well over six feet—allowing for the frightened hunching of his shoulders—and built like a tank. He kept quiet while I explained the problem to the desk sergeant. It's not an easy thing to explain a nut to a cop—with the nut standing right there.

Evidently I managed; we were escorted upstairs to detective country. There were about a dozen grey steel-and-linoleum desks, and four plain-clothes cops. I think we interrupted a pretty good poker game.

I went through the story again; the kid didn't seem to want to add or subtract or change anything. My audience wasn't especially encouraging. I remember wondering, while I talked, what size collar the average plain-clothes cop wears. Eighteen? Nineteen? They might as well leave them in uniform. Finally, I was shown to a chair in a corner of the squad-room, alongside a coffee table piled with back issues of *Penthouse* magazine. (The centrefolds had all been torn out.) The kid disappeared into another room with three of the four detectives.

The cop who stayed with me didn't seem particularly interested in any of it; I don't hate or distrust cops, but I couldn't see any point in trying to strike up a conversation with this one. We communicated by signs: I built a coffee from instant and the electric kettle at the far end of the room; I raised an eyebrow and he pointed out the direction to the can; I pointed to the phone, and he nodded. (It seemed like a good idea to tell the dispatcher what was happening.) We managed to pass an hour without uttering a word to each other. And I found out that *Penthouse* runs some pretty good articles — with and without pussy. There was a really good one about the gasoline price rip-off...

They brought the kid back out to the squad-room, still looking scared but a bit less hysterical. The boss cop manoeuvred me into a corner. "You got a live one here, but he's not dangerous or anything. No record, nothing like that. You want to take it from here? We phoned the brother... there won't be any trouble."

I thought about the money I could have been making on the road, instead of sitting here. I said, "Yeah, sure. I'll take him home. But he's scared shitless... you know that. What'll I do if he starts blubbering again? I don't need it."

"Humour him. Tell him you've got a police escort."

"Do I?"

"Christ, no. How many of us do you see here? Four? Normally it's twenty. It's a shitty night."

"Okay. I'm convinced. But how about the kid?"

"Leave it to me." The cop walked over to the kid. "Mr. Watson, I think we've got this thing under control now. Our plan will work better if you let the cabby drive you home..."

"But they'll follow us! You wanna use me for bait!"

"Oh, I don't think they'll be following you. We've already set our plan in motion . . . they're lying low right now, I'd say." The cop gave me a broad wink.

"But suppose they're not . . . what if they *do* follow us?" The kid looked ready to start crying again.

"Ah, don't you see? Our plan will work that much faster if they *do*. We'll watch you every inch of the way."

"Watch me? How?"

"Unmarked cars, Mr. Watson. I've assigned forty officers to the case, with orders to stay out of sight. You won't see them, but they'll be there. If you sneeze, my men'll know it."

I had to admire that thick-necked cop; it was the finest con-job I've ever seen. The kid seemed to stand a foot taller while his hand was being shaken. Then the cop made a show of shaking my hand, too. He could've crushed cannon-balls with that grip. "Gentlemen, I'm glad you came to us. Don't worry, we'll nail 'em . . . and one day we'll all be able to laugh at this. Good luck!" Another wink— and a clap on the shoulder that could've buckled my knees if I hadn't seen it coming.

I steered that enormous child back out to the cab, wondering how in hell I manage to get into these things—and wondering why more cops don't write books. Maybe they get to the point—I've found myself on the edge of it more than once—where the bizarre and the idiotic and the violent become the stuff of a day's work. It's a cynical, almost encapsulated way to live; I guess that's why a cop is a cop is a cop. No matter what kind of party you invite him to.

Nothing happened during the rest of the trip, of course. Nothing was going to happen in any case, but at least the kid sat a lot straighter in the seat. It's pretty hard to drive more than a couple of blocks at this time of night, without passing a uniform car or a radar cruiser — and anyone who can't recognize the ass end of a Plymouth Fury at three hundred yards, no matter what colour, deserves the speeding ticket he gets. I made a point of slowing down each time we passed a cop car pretending to be invisible on a gas-station lot, and pointing it out to the kid. He seemed to like that.

The brother met us at the curb; he was even bigger than the kid. A nice guy, from what I could make out. He looked up at the sky, then peeled two tens out of his pocket. The fare was eight dollars; I thought about making a token protest.

"Shit!" he said. "That goddam moon again!"

"Will he be all right?" I asked.

"Oh, sure. A day or two . . . it doesn't happen every month."

"He's not always this nervous, then?"

"Are you kidding? He's a middle linebacker on the school football team!"

☞ CAST OF CHARACTERS

☞ Not all of the nuts are in the back seat. It wouldn't work; somebody has to drive the taxi. Take Jay, for instance:

Jay is another of the underemployed, but at least he's going back to college in the fall; and he's one of the lucky ones—he only blew a year or two in this crazy business. I think he might've been a little strange before he came into it.

The Easter Bunny routine sounds like one of Jay's own ideas. I don't know whether the idea came to him first, or whether he just happened across this stupid pink rabbit suit with two-foot ears and figured he'd better do something with it. Anyway, he spent all of Easter weekend driving around in it; and Steve, the boss, had laid on about fifty bucks' worth of candy eggs. The kids loved it; a few drunks must've given it some serious thought. The TV news people got hold of the story, and Jay had a nice three-minute play on the late news the night before Easter.

It was a howl: the only catch was that we started getting calls for cabs from places a hundred miles away. The irony of it is that Jay happened to be dispatching while the TV station ran the tape of his earlier performance. He had to explain to callers why they couldn't have the Cab With The Rabbit.

Jay says his biggest problem was cops: ("What the hell is this? You steal this cab, Mac—or what? Harry, check the radio. See if there's a 'want' on this damned thing.'')

Jay wasn't stopped by *every* cop car he passed—it just seemed that way. He gave away more chocolate eggs to cops than he did to kids. Still, there must be a few guys in blue wondering: "Say, pardner, who *was* that masked rabbit?"

☞ Rog is an elder of his church, but that's not his problem; nor is the fact that he's been happily married for years. And I suppose it doesn't matter that he coaches minor-league hockey, drinks sherry (when he drinks at all), and has probably never been to a poker game or a horsetrack; no one of those things—no four of them, in fact—would be enough to make us wonder about him. But *all five* add up to just too much; sainthood tends to be a gloomy business. Rog couldn't care less.

He compounds the whole thing by taking the taxi game as seriously as a banker takes interest rates. Ask Rog, for instance, how much money he made (and exactly where) on February the fourth ten years ago, between the hours of ten and noon. Give him time to look it up in one of his log-books—it might take a day—and he'll tell you. To the penny.

Most of the guys in our fleet keep their cars clean; Rog makes a fetish of it. To him, the business is a profession; a profitable one. And he looks like a quarterback-turned-preacher.

He makes a hell of a lot of us pretty nervous.

☞ Jimmy had his two-way radio ripped out and went back downtown to play the streets—for about the tenth time. It's a lonesome way to make a living. He's probably better off, though: he hates everybody.

You may recognize Jimmy if you ever happen to flag his cab: he's a big man in his sixties, and he wears a fedora that must pre-date Hitler. The biggest favour he could do you (and himself) is to keep his mouth shut; it's also the *last* thing he's likely to do. Instead, he'll bitch mercilessly about the price of gas and the way the radio fleets are killing him. But he won't mention that he's tried working with half the radio fleets in town — and managed to infuriate a dispatcher almost every time he opened his mike.

He *certainly* won't mention that he takes home between four and five hundred a week, after expenses. There's good money in the taxi business—as long as the cab ownership is in *your* wallet.

Come to think of it, maybe you didn't flag Jimmy, after all; the physical description would fit half the independents in the city — although most of them are a hell of a lot less hostile than Jimmy. It wouldn't be unfair to call most of them cynical, though. They've seen it all, and they've been seeing it for twenty or thirty years.

You might notice that most independent cars look as if they'd just come out of the showroom. It's in the nature of the business, and it's something that the Inspection Office apparently hasn't the wit to acknowledge: a guy driving his own car (hell, it may be his only real asset) will probably keep it in perfect condition. A lawyer managing fifty plates owned by fifty faceless clients in Buenos Aires couldn't care less; a car is just an item in the books.

The independents are the dinosaurs of the taxi game. Some of them almost *look* like cab-drivers. God bless them.

☛ Four-Grand Ernie is my day driver, and Four-Grand is a character. If I had to depend on the brief, bleary conversations we have every morning when I pick him up at four (he drops me off at home) I wouldn't know a damned thing about him; but once in a while I run into him at night — he's usually pretty well oiled — and he opens up a bit. Still, the only thing I really know about him is the fact that he started driving while he was trying to put his head back together after a messy divorce.

In that respect, Four-Grand is like half the guys in the business. Oddly enough—even with the hassles and the general absurdity of the game—driving hack can be good therapy. It's a little bit off to one side of the rat race, and nobody *really* expects anything of you; maybe a couple of years' relief from the pressure of everyone else's expectations is what it's all about. The trick is to know when it's time to get back into the real world again; freedom is addictive. Especially the kind you fall into by mistake.

Four-Grand has a face like a map of Ireland—with wit, temper, and drinking habits to match. He's about thirty-five, and the type older women like to mother. I'd guess he has at least a half-dozen girlfriends—all in their fifties and sixties, all living in the same big low-rental building. I won't identify the address, other than to tell you that the number on the front of the building is Four Thousand.

I don't know how he keeps all his women from finding out about each other (or even if he tries), but it must be tricky, in a place like that. They all probably go to the same shrink, too.

Four-Grand would deny it, but I think he's really laughing at the whole thing. And maybe some of the old folk-stories are true: perhaps older women are more grateful—and easier. Still, Four-Grand is pretty lonesome; it shows through the Irish swagger and the booze, and nobody likes to eat Sunday dinner alone. His routine, every Sunday afternoon, is to arm himself with a case of beer saved over from Saturday — and knock on the doors of his girlfriends' apartments until one of them invites him in for dinner and the evening.

I think he hates me: he asks the same question every morning when I pick him up, and he's asked it every morning for a year: "You wanna start about noon?"

No way. After twelve hours, almost all of them in the dark, I need another twelve hours away from it. "No, Ernie. I don't want to start before four."

"But I gotta be downtown by two!" (What he means, of course, is that he wants to start drinking beer at one.)

"Tell you what, Ernie. Tell Steve when you're quitting, and remind him to send me a cab at about four, okay?" It's almost a ritual: Ernie picks me up (and I take him home) maybe three times a month. The rest of the time I have to depend on Steve's memory— and hope he sends one of my buddies: they charge me a buck to take me to the garage. Rookies and other strangers charge the three-thirty that's usually on the meter. That's life.

But I can't really complain. Repairs, maintenance, and keeping the car clean are the day-driver's responsibility. Four-Grand hasn't let me down yet; we drive one of the best-looking cabs in town. We'll never really be friends, but we understand each other. I always get into a car that's ready to go—and that's half the battle.

I've never really enjoyed driving the day shift; it's just not my style. That probably doesn't sound as if it makes much sense, but there's such a difference in the texture of the business—between night and day—that it's almost impossible for a driver to switch shifts and be comfortable about it. Most of the goofy things happen at night; so does most of the money. If night drivers have the best stories to tell, the guys on the day shift are the earnest plodders who bring it all back to reality. If the night trade is mostly people partying and tripping around on impulse, the day trade is groceries that have to be hauled, women who have to get to the doctor's, and parcels that have to be delivered. If there's a logical reason for the taxi business to exist, the day-time trade provides most of that reason.

But the days plod along, and nothing much happens—and the money is usually terrible. Driving the day shift takes a lot more patience than I've got; which is why we need the stolid characters like Ernie. I have no idea how much money Ernie makes. I could guess at it, by figuring out his mileage for a few days, but it's none of my business. Apparently it's enough to keep him going on his nightly tour of the pubs — although he has to phone the office occasionally, to see if I'm available to take him home for free.

I don't mind; Four-Grand can be pretty funny when he's half in the bag. But, *home*? How the hell can anybody live in a motel for three years?

☛ Iris is one of our legends.

She used to be a truck driver — and that's a few years before Women's Lib declared that *everyone* is entitled to a coronary (or hernia) regardless of sex. I'd guess that Iris was too busy being one of the guys to give a good goddam what the libbers were yelling about. It must've been a bit of a problem for most of her buddies, though: what the hell do you do about this long-haired loudmouth who's as big as you are—and female?

I don't mean to be unkind to Iris; in fact, I rather like her. We've had the occasional long, deep conversation at three in the morning, while we waited for an order to go from some dark and lonely post. I learned that the loudmouth bit was a defence; and God knows everybody could use one. She was always a big girl, but I knew her before she began to put on the extra thirty or forty pounds. In those days, without too much work, she could've been pretty: good eyes, good bone structure, long blonde hair that should have been given a chance to do something for her.

But, obviously, she just wasn't into that kind of thing; she still carries the truck-driver image with her — and there's that extra thirty or forty pounds. And the mouth. You don't recognize Iris by the way she looks; you could be totally blind, travelling through Ankara—and three syllables would tell you that Iris was there.

"How the hell are ya, buddy-boy? Ya still beatin' yer wife, answer yes or no . . . ha, ha! Ya still in the goddam cab business? Yeah . . . no shit! I mean, what else, hey, buddy? . . . Ha, ha! Well, see ya . . . keep yer pecker outta the wrong places, huh?"

It goes on and on — and none of it is really *her*. But midnight psychiatry is still the world's most dangerous game, and I can imagine few more dangerous things than trying to find out what makes Iris tick.

Iris has a voice that really gets to you after a couple of minutes, especially when it filters through the tinny sound of most two-way radios: "Okay, sweetie-baby, here I am, lover. How about a nice order for Iris, hey, baby? I'm ready, doll-baby . . . let's have it. . . ." On and on it goes—as long as she's in radio range.

But most dispatchers have a way of getting her off the air for an hour or so at a time: they give her a shot to the airport, or a couple of parcels going even farther. That keeps her radio transmissions down to about a half-dozen a day—so everyone else can get some work done. Like hauling groceries.

Everybody thinks Iris is crazy, but look at it this way: hauling groceries all day puts maybe fifty dollars on the sheet, and that includes the odd run with a fat lady going to get her new supply of diet pills. A day of running to and from the airport (or wherever) can easily put a hundred on the sheet. Perhaps more.

Sure, Iris is mouthy—and a pain in the ass. But tell me: who's crazy?

☛ There are a lot of solid citizens in this game. It still astounds me that a man could put together a good family life out of driving hack, but it *does* happen.

Like Art, for instance. I don't know this for sure, but I'd guess that Art started to get serious when the baby was born. (Hell, he still goes to every poker game — but he wins a lot.) And I suppose a woman like Carol would tend to keep a guy on the straight road; no man with all his marbles would play games with her.

Art is the kind of guy you're always glad to see, whether you're just sitting on a quiet post, yakking and waiting for an order, or hoisting a couple of midnight beers at the Suburban. He always has a story or two; better still, he knows how to *listen*. We don't see Carol (everyone calls her Chuck) very often, but that makes sense: she looks good, and she's one of those rare girls who just can't help being friendly. But there's no point in inviting awkward situations, and too many of the guys have no women of their own. Art is not stupid.

I have this bad habit: I *like* talking to women, especially the bright ones; it's the only way to find out how half of the human race thinks. And I'm a fan of Chuck's because she's funny and clever and honest. Still, I sometimes wonder what Art thinks when Chuck and I get into one of our marathon conversations. It happens seldom enough: I haven't seen her in almost a year.

But I keep remembering the awesome jealousy of cab-drivers: it would make Othello seem indifferent. I've been caught in the middle often enough to be a bit wary, and probable innocence is no defence in this game. Art's my buddy, though; I think he'll understand if Chuck and I ever get into another four-hour head-to-head dialogue. I sure as hell hope so.

All of which is beside the point, except to show that I like them both. They could be any happy couple, anywhere, and Art could be a stockbroker — for all the difference his *real* trade makes in the way they live. They bought a house last year; a nice one.

Remarkable? Hell, in this business it's damned well miraculous. Art and Carol aren't the only ones who've done it, but a one-armed man wouldn't have to borrow any fingers to add up the total.

☛ Crazy Charlie is a millwright by trade, and he could be earning twelve dollars an hour — or more. But something snapped a few years ago, and the tyranny of the time-clock and the idiocy of half-assed foremen drove him into the cab business. (Most drivers could tell you about half-assed foremen.)

To be strictly accurate, Charlie didn't come *directly* into the taxi game: he spent some time as a bouncer at one of the hairier local pubs. They still talk about the time Charlie grabbed one particularly obnoxious punk by the scruff of the neck and the ass of the pants — and heaved him clear across forty feet of road in front of the joint.

He's a displaced Maritimer with fore-arms like hawsers, and a wit that probably comes as close to Groucho Marx's as anyone's. He has ten thousand friends for every enemy — and I sure as hell wouldn't want to be that enemy. Even some of the guys he had occasion to mangle slightly, during his chores as a bouncer, seek him out just to say hello. (And perhaps to see if he looks as formidable when they're sober as he did when they were blasted. I expect he does.) And if Charlie ever decides you're his friend, you couldn't drive him off with a cannon.

I got stuck out in the boondocks one time. Flat tire. I'd just begun to change the damned thing when Charlie drove up. "You need a hand?"

"Hi, Charlie. Nope, I'm okay. Be finished in a minute. Thanks anyway."

"C'mon, let me at that damn thing!"

"It's all right, Charlie. I've changed a few tires in my time."

"Bullshit! You're not supposed to be liftin' nothin'."

"What do you mean?"

"You just got outta the hospital, for chrissake! Your hernia..."

"Charlie, I had that fixed two years ago! No problem."

"Fuck off! I'm changin' that tire..." There's nothing wrong with being a friend of Charlie's.

He has a lot of fans, too; half the regulars who get into my car ask about him. One of his fans went as far as to phone one of the local newspapers—still laughing—to tell about her ride in Charlie's car. The newspaper sent a reporter to take a ride with him:

"Are you the taxi?"

"No, not personally. I can drive one, though."

According to the reporter, he talks a blue streak. "I'm a hundred-per-cent driver... when I'm not driving a cab, I'm drivin' everybody crazy." On and on Charlie went, according to the story in the paper. "What's the definition of a racetrack?"

The reporter said she'd rather not guess.

"It's a place where the windows clean the people!"

After a few more of these, the reporter said, "I've never been in a cab like this..."

"Neither have I. I just stole it an hour ago!"

 ROYALTY

☛ We don't always see women at their best.

I don't mean that we see them in curlers, no makeup, wearing rump-sprung slacks and ratty sneakers—we do, but that's not what I'm getting at. (Why the hell would they get duded-up to take a cab to the coin-wash, anyway?) And I don't mean some of the young ones with the faces of angels and the mouths of stevedores, or even those occasional (very, very occasional) ones who try to get you to take the fare out in trade. You'd lose on the exchange, most of the time.

What I'm getting at is that strange thing that comes over a lot of middle-class women starting, it seems, at about fifty: they discover their royal blood. (I hasten to add that their numbers are small; the rectal distress they generate makes them seem far more numerous than they really are.) I suppose if you want to practise being a princess your cab-driver is as good a subject as anybody.

☛ Everybody knows—or at least suspects—that we aren't all that crazy about grocery runs. But they're part of the business, and most of the girls are just great; still, you tend to wonder if a ten-dollar trip is being dispatched over your head while you fumble with the trunk key.

Almost nobody knows that the driver is not obliged—by law— to load or unload the bags, although few of the guys are boorish enough to refuse. (Hell, we all need the exercise.) But it *is* an extra

service, and all work has its price. The legal price in this town is ten
cents a bag, to a maximum of thirty cents. Three bags: thirty cents
Fifty bags: thirty cents. One of the first things you learn in this
business is that the more groceries you load, the more hassle you'll
have in trying to collect your lousy thirty cents; it happens often
enough that you have to consider it.

Anyone who thinks Women's Lib is really working would be
astonished to know how few women object when the nearest male
— the driver — takes the chore off their hands. Great. Women
shouldn't be stevedores; but chivalry is one thing and making a
living is another. Thirty cents, please. It's a bargain.

Some of the girls don't understand this.

Madame glided through the automatic doors of the supermarket,
and I was immediately grateful that I didn't work in the place. She
was a procession all by herself, but three red-faced (and obviously
chastised) bag-boys brought up the rear, each manoeuvring two
of those idiot-designed shopping carts toward my car. Madame
manoeuvred nothing but a vast aura of tight-girdled dignity.

I opened the trunk and we set to work. Twenty bags? Thirty? I
began to wonder how many I could stuff into the front seat beside
me; the trunk won't hold more than about fifteen. The bag-boys
evidently knew her as a regular. Their muttered curses did not
imply any great affection for her.

As we wrestled with that ton or more of groceries I noticed that
she remained, poised and regal as hell, by the right rear door of the
car. Queen Victoria would have quailed.

When she realized she had caught my eye she said — in a voice
ringing with majesty — "Don't you open the door for a *lady*?"

I replied, "Yes, madam. *Always!*" And kept on loading the
bags.

☞ Some of them seem to discover their royal blood at about the
time they discover Chanel N° 5. Or maybe it's the other way
around. It doesn't matter. Perhaps the final burning of the mortgage

triggers the whole thing. Whatever. With royalty it's always furs—
and enough perfume to gag a goat.

"Where're we going, ma'am?"

"Just keep heading west. I'll tell you where to turn."

(We all hate that; we just bloody well hate it. It's a bit like telling
a journeyman carpenter which end of the hammer to hold. Some of
us *do* know what we're doing—peasants though we may be—and
we take some small pride in our tiny skills.)

But some people simply take offence at the suggestion that you
might, you just might, know where their street is; so you go along
with it.

"Turn left at the next light." "No, no! I mean right!" (I'm
trapped in the left-turn lane, lady.) "Can't you pass some of this
traffic?" (The road is jammed solid, both ways.) "Turn here!
Here!" (It's the middle of the block, for chrissake!)

She delivers her instructions in tones of command that would
make Napoleon sound like an orderly-room clerk. When we find
the place—and who among us is brave enough *not* to have found it?
— she peers at the meter, snorting her disbelief. Three-twenty. I
hand her the change from her five-dollar bill and she closes her
purse with a *snap!* of triumph.

As if to prove some unprovable point I get out of the car, walk
around the back, and open her door. If she appreciates the small
gesture, she makes no sign. Then, with that straining, heaving
lurch with which so many women leave a car — as if even the
ear-lobe muscles were involved—she releases a rattling, thunder-
ing fart that would derail a streetcar.

I can't resist; I absolutely *cannot* resist:

"Madam, how comforting it is to know that royalty does that
too!"

Her look of pure hatred is worth the price of admission. But
nobody won that particular encounter; even with the windows
rolled down, Chanel N° 5 does *not* blend with whatever else she left
in the car.

☞ Why do they feel they have to smell stronger as they get older?
Or are their furs simply saturated with an accumulation of perfume,
and they can't get it out? And why does the whole thing go with that
air of assumed majesty?

She came out of the subway exit, looking imperious and lost at
the same time. Mink, I suppose.

"Pine Hills Cemetery."

(The breaks of the game. A slow day, and I've been waiting at
the subway for almost an hour—and I get a fare going exactly two
blocks.)

It was a bitter February day, windy and bright. The car was
sealed tight against the cold, and the overpowering miasma of
perfumed furs almost made me want to throw up. I decided that two
blocks was plenty far enough.

"Through the gates, and take the first lane to the right."

I took the turn and followed the narrow, winding road through
the orderly jumble of headstones. Several narrower roads branched
from it at intervals. It's a big place; once you're out of sight of the
street, you don't have much to go by. I watched her in the mirror:
she was lost, and her face began to crumble.

Suddenly, "Here! Stop here!"

It's hard to stop a car smoothly when they yell like that, but I did
my best.

"Yes, this is the place. He's just over that little rise . . ."

I helped her out of the car, and she took my arm. "Up there, just
over the hill." The wind shot icy needles into my face, and the
going was a bit rough on that icy ground. Then: "No. This isn't the
place." Her voice was almost toneless.

We tried a couple more turns, a few more small hills. She seemed
to cling harder to my arm each time we left the car. You can't let it
all go, not when you're wearing mink; but pain is pain. Finally she
broke:

"Oh, my God! I can't find him! God help me, I can't find him!"

Some women still faint, in case you were wondering. She was out for maybe ten seconds, but I managed to keep her from falling into the snow. It must've taken ten minutes to get her back to the car, over those icy hillocks. The wind was like bayonets, and probably a lot worse for her.

Her composure had returned by the time we drove out through those big stone gates. "Back to the subway, please." The command was somewhat softened by the "please"; the voice was as regal as if I hadn't half carried her on that bitter pilgrimage to a grave she couldn't find. Her husband's? A son's? It doesn't matter, except to her.

I guess dignity was all she had left.

She tipped me a dime.

☞ SUPERMAN AND THE TREELOADER

☞ Anyone who thinks there are no practical jokers left should meet Freddie the Treeloader.

By profession Freddie is — believe this — a tree surgeon. Apparently trees don't get sick in the winter, so he spends about half the year driving cab. It's a different game when Freddie's on the road; if he ever gets you in his sights for one of his wildly elaborate projects, you could find yourself looking over your shoulder for the rest of your life. His schemes aren't *always* at the expense of one individual, though. He can victimize whole towns.

There was the time, about a year ago, when he decided to tape a sound documentary based on his somewhat poisonous opinion of Highland Creek, a suburb in the far eastern boondocks. Anyway, Freddie taped this epic — I think it was eight full cassettes — complete with the sounds of gunfire, martial music, a cast of thousands. (The thousands were a half-dozen drivers using different voices. Starvin' Marvin was the voice of the Russian admiral, as I recall.)

"Russian admiral?" you ask. Certainly. Freddie had the whole Soviet fleet shelling Highland Creek from a point a couple of miles offshore in Lake Ontario. And Luftwaffe re-treads bombing the place from the air. The assault troops were either high-school cadets or garbage-truck drivers; I've forgotten which.

The defenders had holed up in the local Legion Hall. There was the usual command-post chatter, then the fade-out to the sound of shells screaming overhead — and the steady clinking of beer bottles. It must have taken Freddie weeks to tape, and it was a classic.

His Superman bit was his best, though. He'd come across this Superman costume somewhere: mask, cape, blue T-shirt with a big red "S"—the works. He *had* to show it to the guys, naturally, so he brought it out to the office one night. After modelling it for the dispatcher and a few of us who'd dropped in for a minute, he slipped into the back room and donned his street clothes over the costume. Then he drove to Millie's Restaurant, a few blocks away.

A few minutes later, he phoned for a cab. The dispatcher was in on the gag, of course, and juggled things so that the order went to some kid who'd been in the business about six hours.

Freddie got into the cab at Millie's—fully clothed—and told the kid to drive him to a certain phone booth at the commuter station a mile down the road. (The place would be deserted at this time of night.)

"Wait for me."

Now — try to imagine the driver's frame of mind as he watched this nut undress in the phone booth and come bounding back to the car, looking like Superman.

"There's trouble at 4301 Kingston. The building's collapsing! Go, man! Go!"

The kid didn't say a word; he just drove to the address, a couple of blocks away. Freddie jumped out of the car, ran up to the front of the big apartment building, and gave the concrete a resounding *whack!* with his fist. He bounded back to the cab, cape flying.

"Very good, my man! That takes care of that! Now, back to the phone booth!"

There, Freddie pulled his clothes back on over the costume. (The driver still hadn't uttered a sound.)

"Good work! Now take me back to Millie's."

At Millie's, Freddie laid the rest of it on the kid: "What? You want money? *Money* . . . for your part in helping those poor souls in that apartment building? Very well. Go back to the office. They know all about this. Just tell them to put it on a company charge.''

The kid actually tried, but you can guess how much luck he had with the dispatcher. Ten minutes later, he was seen parking the cab and talking to himself. It was only eleven p.m.

None of us ever saw or heard from him again. And consider this: he'll never be able to tell anybody about it.

☞ ONE SHOE

☞ I like to think of this story as the Portuguese Connection. It's short, and it doesn't really have an ending. I wasn't even going to tell anybody about it, but the phone was ringing as I walked into the apartment at about two a.m. — and Joan had waited up for me. There was no way to avoid telling her. The phone call was from Stan, the night dispatcher. "Did you turn some guy in to the cops a little while ago?"

"Why?" I wasn't especially proud of it.

"Well, they phoned me about it . . . something about a rapist?"

"I wouldn't know about that. I knew they wanted him, that's all. . . ."

"Well, whatever. You'll be hearing from a Sergeant Brown in a few minutes. He just wanted to confirm a couple of things with me, first. You wanta tell me about it some time?"

"Sure, Stan. I'll tell you about it . . . some time."

"You luck onto some real beauts, don't you? G'night, guy."

"Good night."

Joan did just about everything but grab the phone from my hand.

"Who was that, at this hour?"

"Stan, the dispatcher. You know Stan . . ."

"Of course I know Stan. But why was he calling you in the middle of the night?"

"It's the middle of the afternoon for him."

"Cute. Now, what was that all about? What happened?" She almost stamped her foot in exasperation; she worries when I drive nights.

So, I went over the whole thing for her:

It must've been about ten o'clock when the evening dispatcher cracked: "Hey, gentlemen. I just had a call from the police about some joker running around West Hill in one shoe. They must want him pretty bad . . . and they said, don't pick him up, he's probably carrying. And he's Portuguese, they said. So let me know if you see him, okay?"

I filed it in the back of my head and promptly forgot all about it.

Business kept humming until about midnight, then with the snow falling steadily the entire ass fell right out of it. By one o'clock I'd had enough; with Joan staying over, there was no way I was about to grind out the whole shift. Joan is good to come home to, and this was the time. I pulled into the all-night gas bar a couple of blocks from the garage. I was just finishing the totals on the trip-sheet when I heard a tapping on my window. I looked up.

The guy was young, curly-haired, European-looking. I nodded. I watched him walk around the front of the car and climb into the back seat on the other side. "Danforth and Pape." The accent was thick and Mediterranean: Greek? No . . . and not Italian, either. Spanish, maybe. There was something else about him that kept nudging the back of my mind, but I couldn't quite catch it.

I hadn't really wanted another fare—and Joan was waiting—but another seven or eight dollars couldn't hurt. I swung through a U-turn and headed west. Funny: most men (except for some of the heavy-executive types) will climb into the front seat when they're alone. But this guy was no executive, and he started to go through one of the damnedest performances I'd ever seen: lie down on the back seat, moan, sit up and stare through the rear window as if he thought we were being followed, lie down, moan some more . . . sit up and check the scenery again. It was not a calming experience —and nobody acts like that, not even drunks.

Two things hit me at once. The dispatcher's earlier warning about the nut loose in West Hill—and the way this guy had walked around the front of the car: he'd been *limping*. A guy with one shoe in an inch of new snow would limp, and he'd probably moan with the pain of a frozen foot. And maybe the accent wasn't Spanish; how about Portuguese? The cops had said he might be armed.

I felt as if I had suddenly come down with a case of terminal stupidity. My fare wasn't threatening at all, but I didn't need his kind of action — especially when he fitted the cop bulletin perfectly. What now? No point in trying to use the radio: he'd hear it. And where in hell are all the cops? On any other night, we would've passed a dozen cruisers. Finally I spotted one waiting for a stoplight, heading in the opposite direction. This had to be the time. I hung a hard left, against the red light, and stopped the car with the right side almost touching the bumper of the cruiser. I jammed the shift lever into Park, jumped out, and started running.

A manoeuvre like that tends to get a cop's attention. The two of them were out of the cruiser, guns drawn, by the time I reached the back of my own car. The whole scene became a blur; two good cops can move pretty fast, and my fare was in the back of the cruiser, probably cuffed, by the time I could've counted to ten.

The big cop walked over to me. "I assume there's a story here. Do I get to hear it?" He seemed about as friendly as a harness cop ever gets. I croaked something that probably didn't make much sense. "Okay," the cop said, "just relax. You were either in trouble, or you're an idiot. Idiots drive like that, but you don't look like an idiot. Tell me about it."

I was able, finally, to tell him about the "want" on my fare. He checked it through his own division by radio; he said, "I think maybe we owe you a beer. This guy's a real sweetheart." The other cop took down the details, including my name and phone number. "Yeah, I think you did us a favour." I still didn't feel right about it; he hadn't done me any harm. Maybe I had panicked over nothing.

Later, Joan said: "But you *had* to turn him in! Who knows *what* he might've done? After all, the police wanted him . . . isn't that enough?''

I thought: Maybe not.

The phone rang again: "Sergeant Brown, Metropolitan Police, here. I wanted to tell you about the subject you turned in to us a while ago.''

"Yeah? What'd he do? I feel kind of funny about the whole thing. . . .''

"You do? Why?''

"Well, he never did me any harm. . . .''

"So you were lucky. We've known this cat for years. Weapons, B. and E., you name it. You're thinking maybe you turned in a good guy, by mistake?''

"Well . . .''

"Forget it. You're lucky your ass is still in one piece. Okay, I'll tell you something that might make you feel a little better. We're pretty sure he raped a thirteen-year-old about a half-hour before you picked him up. Everything fits: the time, the description, everything. We figure he's a cinch for it . . . and we've got a half-dozen other rapes that look good on him. Does that help?''

"A little, maybe . . .''

"Just what does it take with you, mister? You did us a favour, and you'll be getting a letter of commendation from the department. We owe you, whether you like it or not.''

Joan gave me hell for taking a chance like that — and I never got my letter of commendation. I don't even know if the guy turned up guilty.

☞ THE TIME HARRY DIDN'T PAY THE RENT

☛ Harry was a compulsive entertainer. You'd know that, just from hearing him tell a couple of his stories to a tableful of drivers at the Suburban. He reminded me of things I'd read about those travelling minstrels who wandered through the Middle Ages, drawing whole villages for audiences. His delivery was something like Orson Welles doing Johnny Carson, with material straight out of Runyon. And he had a stock of dirty stories that would keep a cheap nightclub act going for years. The action was always at Harry's table, wherever he went.

It's not that he was any kind of hero; the thought would've embarrassed hell out of him. But he knew everybody and he'd been everywhere — to hear him tell it. Just how much we believed is beside the point; some of his yarns were a little hard to swallow. Like the one about the big downtown poker games he'd been in. But it didn't matter a damn: Harry was *funny*. And he loved an audience.

That's why his disappearance—literally overnight—caused so much speculation; and why the rumour-mill churned out such stupefying bullshit. Harry was in jail. He was in the fracture ward of some hospital. Harry was on the run from some of the downtown boys. He was driving hack in New York. Someone was sure he saw him at the track yesterday. Harry was dead.

There was never any real likelihood that he was dead, as far as we could figure; but a couple of the other possibilities made some

193

sense. A few of us knew, for instance, that Harry had been getting in deeper and deeper over his head; almost every day for the last few weeks there'd been phone messages over the air. They were always the same: "Four-two . . . call Mr. Glickman, right away."

Anyone who's been in the game more than a couple of years gets to recognize some of the downtown names; this one belonged to a heavy character with a sizeable chunk of the rougher taxi action. Nobody could be happy about that kind of message, but Harry wasn't much of a worrier. Perhaps he should've been.

I should explain how these things work:

A driver on a regular "split" can make a living, but it's no way to get ahead. (For years, it was the only legal way for a driver to operate, but nobody paid much attention to that. It's still the way most owners prefer to have their cabs working.) You can't get in over your head, and it's simple: you gas up the car at the end of every shift and split what's left of the take fifty-fifty with the owner. Not much of a carrot.

The guys with a little more imagination shop around for an owner who'll rent his car out by the week or the month. There are a dozen variations on the system, but let's say he rents it out as a package: car, taxi plate, radio, insurance, brokerage dues. He wants three hundred a week, and the driver pays for repairs. There are two things to watch: the owner's reputation — some are a bit hairy, especially when it comes to pressuring people who owe them money—and the condition of the car. The system, in all its various forms, is called a "deal".

Oddly enough, about half the cabs in town are owned by people whose emotional involvement in the taxi business is not conspicuous — lawyers, merchants, real-estate brokers — people who simply couldn't imagine getting behind the wheel. To these gentlemen, the vagaries of the business are meaningless, the driver strictly a nameless irritation—and the car an object to be driven, as far as possible, at a maintenance cost of zero.

And Harry, in his search for a "deal", had walked straight into it. The car had looked good, but there had been well over a hundred thousand hard miles on it before Harry got it; God knows if it had ever seen any kind of regular attention. It started to fall apart immediately—in all the urgent, expensive ways that a car can ruin you. Glickman was managing the package for some faceless corporation in Boston, which will give you some idea of how much manoeuvring room Harry really had when the rent situation started to get tight.

It's a circular horror. You can't pay the rent if the car's off the road; if you spend a couple of hundred dollars to put the car back in business, you haven't enough left to pay the rent. And somewhere in the middle of it, you have to live.

Personally, I'd never do business with one of the downtown heavies—on any basis. Life's too short, and the word is that they can make it shorter. (Not directly, of course; nobody does that kind of thing any more. But some of them know how to make you old, too soon.) I have nothing against Glickman, and I don't know if I should. With luck, I'll never meet him.

Harry was gone about six months. He never talks about it. In fact, Harry doesn't talk much about anything. He comes out and drives the odd Friday or Saturday night—when he can get a car—but no more stories, no more audiences. He doesn't really avoid us. Not quite.

I don't know what happened to Harry, and I don't expect to find out. But I know how he looks. There isn't a mark on him, although his shoulders are a bit hunched and he tends to look to the side without moving his head. And he never makes a quick movement of any kind.

There may be nothing to it, but I can't help remembering something I read a long time ago. It was about what happens to you after a thorough, strictly professional beating—by guys you don't even know.

☞ LEGAL EAGLE

☞ Some of us talked about hiring a lawyer — or several — but we never got around to it, probably because the whole damned business was so stupid and embarrassing.

Being charged as a found-in is not one of the classier ways of getting into trouble; but we'd done it. All sixty-one of us. And here we were, milling about the lobby of the courthouse, looking foolish. The usual penalty is peanuts; a small fine, ten or twenty dollars — and a record. If there's one thing you don't need in this business, it's a record.

Every so often one of the guys would stroll over to study the docket posted by the courtroom doors, as if to see if this thing could really be happening to us.

It was.

J. B. and Barney were right at the top of the list. The charge was "keeping a common gaming house" — a much heavier rap than just being caught in the damned place.

I hate surprises. I decided to see how it went with J. B. and Barney, rather than wait outside for my name to be called.

I closed the big doors behind me and looked around the courtroom. It was like Old Home Week: wives, girlfriends, brothers, bookies. Everybody knew everybody. Standing-room only.

The judge was one of the biggest men I'd ever seen — and black. He was talking to Crown counsel, and his voice was like the rumble of summer thunder.

197

☛ I have to go back a bit. For one thing, J. B. needs some explaining. He looks like a retired jockey, and I think he'd like the description; there can't be a horsetrack in the country that he hasn't played at one time or another. He's about five feet, stocky, red-faced—and just about hyper enough to walk three feet off the ground. He has a slight stammer when he's really up. With or without the stammer, he is not known for his tact, especially after a good night at the track and a taste of the grape afterwards. Men of some forbearance have been known to reward J. B.'s occasional lapses with a good rap on the mouth. Still, I doubt that he has any serious enemies.

J. B. was the organizer and guiding genius of the project that got us all into this mess.

It really began the night Barney was stabbed. He'd gone to the rescue of another driver, and it nearly cost him his life. With a wife and kids to feed—and with the Workmen's Compensation Board clearly suspicious of claims by cab-drivers, especially those who fall into this kind of trouble—Barney needed money.

We all wanted to help out. Hell, there just wasn't any way we'd let Barney and his family go on Welfare.

☛ There was nothing wrong with J. B.'s idea: a benefit stag, with the admission price and a percentage from the table to go to Barney. But I'd like to know what the committee was smoking when the *size* of the party was decided. You just can't advertise these things to the immediate world. Someone decided that we weren't going to have a big enough turn-out, and started selling tickets at the neighbourhood pub. If ever there was an invitation to disaster, that was it. You could sell tickets to a gang-rape in that joint—and still wonder if you were getting a good enough class of people.

But, with one exception, the stag came off as planned: a dozen poker tables, a salami-rye-bread-and-potato-salad buffet, a bar (unlicensed), no fights. There was some entertainment consisting of studies of the nude female form—and it is a measure of the

prurience of this entertainment that not one poker game was interrupted by so much as the flicker of an eyelash.

Some of us hadn't come to play poker, so we watched the girls. I
hoped I wasn't the only one who appreciated the spectacle of fifty
card-players sternly ignoring a bunch of naked women prancing in
their midst.

And I wasn't the only one, as it happened. My friend Mike
looked puzzled for a moment, then started to howl at the whole
absurd scene. Just as suddenly, he stopped laughing and jabbed me
with his elbow.

"Those guys at that table . . . over there, in the corner. They're
not cab-drivers!"

I followed the direction of Mike's gaze: they certainly weren't
cab-drivers. The shirts were too bright, the jackets too mod, the
ties . . . (ties?) . . . but that says it all. They sure as hell were
emphatically *not* drivers!

Mike and I might've made it to the door if we hadn't tried it
together.

Suddenly the place looked like a Giles cartoon: cops everywhere
— pink shirts, checked jackets, canary shirts, polka-dot ties —
everywhere. And more coming in the door. There were about ten
windows in the room, and every one of them contained the ass of
a driver on his way out.

We found out, later, that the building was surrounded by uni-
formed cops; the few who made it through the windows didn't get
very far. Someone had decided that this was a rather important
poker party. It was odd: the table stakes couldn't have been more
than ten bucks a hand.

The cops were polite enough; some of them even had the grace to
act a bit embarrassed by the whole thing. At least no one was
seriously hassled, as far as I know. The procedure was simple: you
had to have a blue ticket to get past the cops at the door. You got
your blue ticket by waiting your turn, then sitting with a cop at one
of the poker tables and giving him your name and address.

The blue tickets looked exactly like traffic summonses.

☞ Crown counsel was an eager young man, full of his own importance. I wondered how many political careers had been launched from the prosecutor's table in a county courtroom. This one seemed to be thinking the same thoughts; he attacked our case as if all sixty-one of us had conspired to dynamite a kindergarten.

The Judge didn't appear to be buying. He rested his chin in his hands, smiling, while the Crown recited the particulars of the case.

Then, in that booming voice: "Is the Crown quite finished?"

"Uh . . . not quite, Your Worship. I have a few more . . . "

"Are they important? Are you going to tell us anything new?"

"Ahh, no . . . I guess not. No." The young man shuffled some papers and sat down.

"Very well, then. I think it's time we heard from the defendants in the first charge. John Bannion and . . . " the Judge studied the docket " . . . Byron Lawson."

J. B. and Barney stood straighter. Barney still looked like hell; which was probably the best way to look, under the circumstances.

J. B., always impatient, raised his hand as if asking permission to leave the room. "Your Honour, I represent B-Barney, here . . . and all the other d-defendants. If it please the C-Court."

"You are Mr. Bannion?" The Judge tried to hide a smile behind his hand.

I thought: Beautiful! Here's where a ten-dollar fine turns into a year in the slammer. I wondered if I had the right to stand up and shout, "Objection!" I decided that probably wasn't one of this Judge's favourite words.

"Hmm." The sound rolled out of that big frame. "I can't say I like this, Mr. Bannion. Are you sure the other defendants *want* you to speak for them? You're on trial, yourself . . . "

"Well, the whole thing was my idea. The stag, I mean . . . and the other guys got no lawyers, anyway."

"You're taking on quite a responsibility, you know. All right, then. Just try to keep it simple. I'll stop you if you start getting in too deep."

The Judge leaned back in his chair and smiled at the Crown.

Crown was not amused.

J. B. is far from stupid, but a Melvin Belli or J. J. Robinette he is not. He began rather badly:

"This stinks! This whole damn thing stinks, Your Honour..."

The Judge leaned forward. "Mr. Bannion! Control yourself! I said I'd help you, but I'm not going to listen to a tirade. Just calm down."

"Yessir. Sorry. B-but I still think it's a hell of a thing when a bunch of working guys get b-busted for trying to help a friend!"

The Judge looked at Crown counsel, then at J. B. "What's this all about? What do you mean, 'trying to help a friend'? What friend?"

"Him!" J. B. said, pointing at Barney.

Crown seemed about to speak, then thought better of it. Barney looked embarrassed.

"You'd better tell us about it, Mr. Bannion. And keep it calm; just the facts, please. Go ahead."

J. B. took a deep breath and began the story of the attack on the other driver, the stabbing, Barney's brush with death. He didn't stammer more than once or twice. "...and so we had a stag, Your Honour. It was the only way we knew... to help him pay the rent and buy some groceries. If anybody's to blame, it's m-me."

"Is this true, Mr. Lawson?"

"Yes, sir, Your Honour." Barney's voice was thin and weak; it hung in the silence of the courtroom.

The Judge drummed his fingers on the desk for a moment. He turned to the Crown.

"Mr. Wright, I think this would be a good case to dismiss. Were you aware of the reasons behind this so-called stag?"

Crown obviously hadn't expected the question, but he answered manfully: "Yes, Your Worship, I was. But I see no reason not to proceed..."

"Hmm. I can think of several. Just what do you propose here?"

"The Crown intends to show that these men knowingly broke the law, and that society cannot tolerate . . ."

"Oh, come now, Mr. Wright! We're dealing with a poker game, not the sanctity of motherhood!"

Crown apparently had a thing or two to learn about judges; he made the mistake of trying to reply in capital letters:

"With all Respect, Your Worship, the Crown Objects to the Suggestion by Your Worship, that This is a Matter to be Taken Lightly. The Law Distinctly Provides . . ."

The Judge raised a huge hand; his face, relaxed to this point, became black granite. Crown stopped in mid-oratory.

"First, Mr. Wright, I will *not* be lectured on the law in this case. Second, I do *not* take lightly the fact that sixty people could leave this courtroom with criminal records . . . for doing something we've all done at one time or another without being caught. In fact, I'd like to know how this . . . party . . . came to attract the attention of almost an entire police division."

"But the Law, Your Worship . . ."

"You're doing it again, Mr. Wright. Just do yourself a favour and listen for a moment. I want this case dropped. Can you agree with that?"

Crown looked shaken, but he stuck to his guns: "No, Your Worship, I can't agree. But I'd go along with suspended sentences."

"Not good enough. Very well, then. Since you can't accept my suggestion, I'll *show* you now it's going to be. Bailiff!"

☛ The scene that followed probably didn't do any real damage to Crown counsel's political career, although he must have wondered why he had decided to make a minor crusade of our case.

The Judge had done whatever judges do, to move quickly from one case to another. The bailiff stuck his head out the courtroom doors and began calling the names of the sixty-one of us who were up on the found-in charge. We were called in groups of ten.

The charge was read once to each group; our names were read separately. The bailiff—a good guy—told us what to expect and what to do. Each of us said, "Guilty!" when his turn came.

After each group of ten, the Judge banged his gavel and boomed: "Absolute Discharge!" During the pauses, and while names were being shouted by the bailiff, the Judge would smile, almost benignly, at the Crown.

I should explain that an absolute discharge is a device by which the court recognizes your guilt, but declares that it won't punish you. It carries no criminal record, and I don't think the Crown can appeal it. Very neat.

The whole thing took about an hour.

Barney and J. B. had a little more to answer to: there was the business of the unlicensed bar—which, of course, the government took as a direct affront—and the matter of the naked girls. (It's a shame the Judge couldn't know how few of the guys paid any attention to them.)

Somebody had to take a fall for all that splendid police work, so Barney and J. B. came out of it with three months' probation. I guess even judges have to deal, once in a while.

☛ J. B. should've let it ride. Three months' probation is a hell of a lot better than some of the alternatives. But, being Irish, he had something much more important on his mind:

"But, the booze, Your Honour! What about that?"

"The booze? What do you mean?"

"The stuff that was on the bar! It cost us over three hundred bucks, goddam it! What happens to that? The cops scooped the whole bloody thing!"

The Judge leafed through the small stack of papers on his desk. "Ah, yes... here we are. Well, I'm afraid that reverts to the Crown, Mr. Bannion."

"You mean the cops drank it."

"I mean, Mr. Bannion, that you've done rather well here today, and it's not too late to change that. I suggest you quit playing lawyer while you're ahead. Now, good day. I trust I won't be seeing you again."

☛ The courthouse lobby was jammed: girlfriends, bookies, the lot of us—all congratulating each other.

Some of the guys had taken the day off, but most had their cabs parked outside. Passers-by must have wondered what the hell was going on, especially since the police station is part of the same building.

A few of the cops who had busted us were there, trying to be friendly. Nobody paid much attention.

Mike said, "Shit! It's noon! There's the day, shot. What'll we do now?"

Someone (I think it was Scotty) said, "*I* know! Let's have a stag!"

☞ FOR SERVICES RENDERED

☛ Cold. Oh, my Jesus, it was cold.

It had quit snowing, but the wind whipped up the fine snow that lay on the ground and drove it in flat, blinding trails that could've been smoke — until you remembered that it was just too goddam cold for a fire to *light*. The roads were a mess. The ploughs and salt trucks had been working like a good thing all night, but the wind shoved the snow back into the streets until the whole thing became a shitty, white mass of snow-and-ice that was just murder.

Nothing was happening. It's a fair bet that three out of every five cars on the road were cop cars; and there wasn't a damn thing to prowl for. Nothing. I think there were three of us idiots still out, trying to make those last, few dollars. The whip antenna moaned in the wind like some exotic kind of feline gone mad.

The dispatcher's voice: "Hey, one of you gentlemen wanna make ten bucks? It's a boost, and the guy doesn't have cables. Anybody around Markham and Lawrence with cables?"

I grabbed the mike. "I'm right on the corner, Donnie..."

"You got cables?"

"No, but I can give him a jack-start."

"Okay, you got it. A brown Camaro, right behind the library. He said ten bucks..."

(You don't know about a jack-start? I'll tell you: it's the hard way to do it, but at least it's a way. You run your front bumper up against the front bumper of the car that needs a boost, and leave your car idling in Drive. That gives you a good ground contact. Then you arrange the bumper-jack and the jack-handle so as to make contact between positive battery terminals of the two cars—and crank the dead car. It works. It works a lot better than cheap cables.)

Speaking of cheap:

We worked on that motherin' Camaro for a half-hour. For openers, that clown had to have been parked there for at least a week; the engine compartment was so jammed full of snow that I could see the indentations of the hood cross-bracing when I opened it up. The cold turned my hands to ice while I brushed away some of that white crud from around the distributor and plugs; it was obvious that this whole goddam thing wasn't going to work.

While I dug away, I said, "This isn't going to work, you know."

"Sure it will! I gotta get home." He kept his hands in his pockets.

"Well, we can try, but I'm tellin' you—*nothing* could start this car as long as it's got a ton of snow under the hood."

"*Sure* it'll work. Just keep tryin'."

So we tried. We tried until my hands felt as if they were frozen to the bumper-jack forever, while he sat in the Camaro — with the door closed — trying the starter switch. The wind blew the snow around the engine as fast as I could brush it away. And there was no way. Nothing in the world was going to make that mother go until she dried off. She turned over all right, but she didn't kick out so much as a popcorn fart.

Enough is enough. I said, "Look. We're wasting our time. The only way to get this thing started is to haul it to a garage and let the snow melt off it. My hands are killing me. I think you said ten dollars . . . ?"

"The hell with *that* noise! I said ten bucks to get it started. You didn't start it, so I'm payin' you nothin'."

"Christ himself couldn't start that sucker, and you know it! I'm supposed to blow a half-hour of my time and freeze my balls off in

this shit for *nothing*? What kind of asshole *are* you? I'm callin' the
cops..."

Donnie had them there in three minutes, but there wasn't much
they could do. Oh, they tried, but they couldn't make it stick —
because there was nothing on the meter. Finally, they got him a
tow-truck to haul the car to the nearest all-night garage.

I guess it was about three hours later when Donnie said: "I think
I got a friend of yours on the line. He wants a cab from the Gulf
Station. How about it?" By this time, mine was probably the only
cab within ten miles.

I said, "Sure, why not?" If I couldn't get my money this time, I
might at least have the pleasure of dumping his ass in a snowbank
somewhere. At first I thought he wasn't going to get into the car,
but he did.

He said, "Oh. It's you."

"Yeah. It's just little ol' me. How far out of your way would you
like me to dump you?"

"I guess you're pretty sore..."

"Goddam right I'm sore! You rip me for ten bucks, and it'll be a
year before I'm warm, again. Yeah, I'm sore. I've met some cheap
bastards in my time..."

"Okay, okay! So I was wrong." I learned that the garage had
kept the Camaro on the hoist, right up near the heaters, till most of
the snow had melted. Then a damned good mechanic had worked
on it for another hour—with no more luck than I'd had.

Then my fare said, "How much?"

"To where?" He gave me the address: a two-dollar run.

I said, "That'll be fifteen dollars, plus tip. Or you damned well
walk." The night was still a vicious mess of bitter, blowing snow,
and the busses had quit running hours ago.

He shrugged. When we got to his place, he left a twenty on the
seat and walked into the house. He probably wasn't a bad guy.
I guess we all have our moments.

☞ ALL IT TAKES IS A PHONE CALL

☛ The mills of God don't always grind slowly — or exceeding small. You can rape a ten-year-old and be out on bail three hours after the cops nail you; all it takes is a phone call to the right lawyer. Or you can be the victim of a savage beating — and wait a year before you can enjoy the tiny satisfaction of seeing your mugger convicted in court. (He'll probably draw three months, to be served on alternate Sundays.) That's a pretty coarse grind.

Exaggeration? Read the papers: such things *do* happen.

Justice shouldn't be the goat; her blindfold is supposed to be symbolic, not real. But the people who run the system have long since bought their way out of the those layers of society in which violence really *means* anything; half of them have never seen anyone over the age of ten make a fist in anger.

Victims—and cops—deal with the brutal smash of a heavy hand, the flash of the blade, the bright deafening blast of the gun. Maybe there's no way to bring these things to the courtroom, no way to help judges and lawyers understand what they *really* mean while they're happening. Judges and lawyers — the good ones — must surely despair at what they see every day in court. But the courtroom is an antiseptic place of pre-trial reports and depositions (all cleanly and freshly typed); a place where learned men in two-hundred-dollar suits fence with rounded phrases, some of them in Latin.

The filth and the pain and the reality seldom get inside the doors.

209

Like the time Al was hassled by the nut with the knife:

He managed, somehow, to grab the mike just long enough to tell
us where he was going and it couldn't have been more than
forty-five seconds before three of us had shrieked to a halt, boxing
his cab in against the curb. Something like half the fleet was there
within a couple of minutes, and it was a sorry-looking punk we
turned over to the cops when they arrived. No, we didn't beat on
him. Most of us aren't hard cases — in spite of what you may
believe — and we figured the sudden sight of twenty angry drivers
would convey all the message anyone should need. Not so, as it
turned out; I guess the only thing some of these clowns understand
is *pain*.

This one was a slow learner. He was out on bail before sunrise —
with his knife, for God's sake — and hailed another cab right
outside the cop shop. He stole eighty dollars from the driver and cut
him for about fifteen stitches, but the cops had him back in the drum
within the hour. I like to think that they chatted with him a little
more directly than we had. (It happens.) They hate having to arrest
the same idiot twice in the same shift; it complicates the paperwork,
for one thing.

The court case came up, finally, and a few of us went along to
keep Al and the other driver company. In this game, you learn
better than to expect too much:

The punk drew six months' probation. I suppose he still carries
the blade.

And then there was the Stoddart murder case.

This one really stung us because we'd all been so involved when
it happened. Justice took a screwing right at the start: one of the
suspects got out on bail — on a murder rap. His own mother turned
him back in almost immediately. She knew.

I can't really say that politics were involved — but I can guess.
There must've been times during the trial when Justice wanted to
rip off the blindfold to see just what in hell was going on. The police
had given this one their very best shot, and in this town their best

shot is very damned good, indeed. But the defence lawyers, with arguments that had to be among the weakest in the history of criminal law, won in a walk.

Let me go back a little:

I hadn't seen Keith in years: an ex-neighbour and a good friend, now a Justice of the Peace. We'd just happened to drop into the same unlikely place for a beer and a sandwich. Like old friends everywhere, we talked about everything—including the upcoming trial.

He said, "Don't depend on those little buggers getting the full treatment."

"Why not?"

He looked at his beer, then at me: "I used to work for the Department of Justice . . . remember?"

"Yeah . . . ?"

"So I keep in touch with my old buddies, and the word is out. This case could blow up into a racial thing, and the department doesn't want that."

"A racial thing? What's *that* got to do with anything?"

"At least one of 'em was in the country illegally, and Immigration is already up to its ass in trouble. The department is not goin' to take a bath just because some cabby got himself shot."

"What're you telling me, Keith?"

"I'm telling you that a lot of important people would just as soon see the case swept under the rug . . . partly, anyway."

"Just because the guy was only a cab-driver . . . ?"

"Don't be paranoid. But you're right, in a way . . . if he'd been some real big-shot . . . "

"Can they really do this?"

Keith puffed out his cheeks, then took a sip of his beer. "I hate like hell to shatter your illusions . . . but, yes, they probably can."

"I don't believe it! What the hell, we've got laws . . . "

"Sure we have. And ninety-nine times out of a hundred—hell, far more than that—the government wouldn't interfere on a bet.

But this case is different, believe me.''

"Keith, it's gotta be bullshit!''

"Okay. You obviously think they can't influence each other. But think about it. Where the hell did half of them go to school together? And the clubs. Do you think the Minister of Justice couldn't walk into the York Club for lunch? Do you think a judge couldn't wander into the Rideau Club? Use your head, for Christ's sake!''

"So they tell a judge what to do . . .''

"Nope. That's too tricky, and most judges would raise supreme shit. But it doesn't matter. The prosecutor . . . the Crown . . . is where it all happens.''

"How is that?''

"Simple. A rookie can be appointed to the case . . . or a damned good man who's ready to collapse from overwork. That's how.''

"What'll happen?'' I asked.

"I figure this way, and it's only an educated guess: the top sentence will be five years . . . and prob'ly one of 'em will get off entirely. That's the way Immigration would like it, as far as I can make out. Don't quote me. I only know what I hear.''

Keith *had* to be wrong; the bastards *couldn't* do that. Could they?

The trial puzzled us. The gun held to the back of the head has to be the ultimate horror; what the bullet does is obscene, distorting the face terribly and making the eyes bulge as if they stood out on stalks. A head shot, at zero range, is a shockingly vicious piece of work that doesn't allow much speculation about the gunman's intentions.

The defence argued, naturally enough, that the whole thing was just a tragic accident: three fine young men had found themselves in the wrong place at the wrong time — and somebody got dead. Terrible. Tragic. But an accident; boys will be boys. Perhaps, if the victim hadn't chosen to drive a cab that night . . .

The Crown had done his homework, but we were disappointed that he chose to counter the defence with high-sounding talk about

Public Indignation and how The Law Was Not Fooled by any of
this nonsense about an Accident . . .

I have a few questions for the lawyers:

If you buy a gun, is that an accident? If you load it and carry it
with you for a night on the town, is that an accident? If you cock it
and hold it to a man's head, is *that* an accident? The gun discharges
—maybe your arm was jostled or you had a sudden, nervous twitch
—and a man lies dead in a splatter of blood and brains. Tell me: at
what point, precisely, did the "accident" happen?

Five thousand cab-drivers would like to know. We're rather
vulnerable; trouble usually starts behind our backs.

My friend Keith was a little off the target: there was only one
conviction. Five years for manslaughter.

The day the decision came down my fare asked me to turn up the
music radio for the nine o'clock news. The first item was the
Stoddart verdict—the trial had been expected to end that evening—
and I'd heard the verdict an hour earlier. The air had been hot with
it, and I suppose every cab-driver in town felt betrayed.

My fare began to curse: "Those bastards! Those stupid, ignorant
cocksuckers! They let those assholes get away with it!"

I'd been plenty shook at the verdict an hour earlier, but I had to
wonder at my fare's violent reaction. "You a cab-driver, too?"

"No, but I just got out of the can last week . . . three bloody
years . . . Jesus Christ!"

"Three years? For what?"

"Would you believe for receivin' stolen goods? I bought a
slightly warm TV from a buddy."

"You got three years for *that*?"

"Hell, I *did* three years — with some time off for keepin' my
nose clean. And that sonofabitch will prob'ly do *two* years for
blowin' a guy's head off . . . shit!"

Yeah. Shit.

☛ Immigration started to do its thing, but a deportation order takes
a while to carry out. Before he finally left, one of those three "fine

young men'' managed to become the prime suspect in a spectacularly vicious beating. The cops cleaned it up with their usual efficiency: about a dozen witnesses, the works. The kind of case a prosecutor just loves to sink his teeth into.

I'm not sure whether the case came to trial, or the Crown decided to drop it. All of a sudden there were no witnesses—not a damned one. Suborned, dead—or just scared off, one way or another? The police would know; but it's all over now, and they have a whole new army of punks to worry about.

That Fine Young Man went home. At last report (it was in all the papers) he'd been charged with something like nineteen armed robberies, back in Jamaica. Nice kid.

☛ I sometimes wonder what Stoddart's widow must feel about all this. And I just hope to hell Keith was wrong. Dead wrong.

☞ COPS AND ROBBERS

☞ Corner shots, at four in the morning, are not my favourite kind of fare—and I didn't much like the look of the two of them when they came out of the phone booth.

The one wearing the Snoopy helmet climbed into the back and said. "Thirty-four Bright Street. The short way."

The skinny one climbed in beside me. "That's near River and King," he said.

Wonderful. Thanks, kid. The worst street in the toughest part of Cabbagetown.

Then the argument started.

Snoopy leaned over the front seat. "I been thinkin'," he said, "let's go to my place instead."

Skinny turned to face him. "What the hell for? There's nothin' to do at your place . . ."

Nothing to do. At four in the morning?

"C'mon . . . we'll go to my place. The old man's still up. He'll pay the cab."

"Like shit he will!"

"Sure. Your old lady never has any money anyway."

"Fuck off! The welfare came today . . . she'll pay!"

They went around a few more times; and all the while, Snoopy kept tapping on my shoulder for emphasis. It's a gesture I hate, even from a friend—I sure as hell don't like it when a stranger does it. I felt like slugging the kid. Christ, it wasn't even my argument!

215

If I'd had to guess at their ages I'd have said about sixteen, maybe seventeen; an undernourished seventeen, at that. But now I was getting a little tired of the whole scene. There are worse things than not being paid your fare; I pulled over to the side of the road and stopped the car. We had a long way to go yet — better to get stiffed for two bucks than for ten.

"Look, guys," I said, "you got no money, right? If it's going to be a problem, why don't you hitch-hike or take a bus? The ride's on me if you want to get out right here."

Skinny flashed me a big smile. "No, man! It's not like that at all! There's money at home . . . you'll get paid. Really!"

"Okay. Just don't try to con me. It's a lot more trouble than it's worth."

"Sure, man. Don't worry."

"So where are we going? You decided yet?"

Snoopy said, "Bright Street, like I told you." He leaned back. I watched him in the rear-view mirror.

The argument was over; they both relaxed and started talking about the party they'd just left. They were stoned on something, but not especially menacing. And what could these two pasty-faced punks do, besides run off without paying?

Skinny said, "We been at the zoo all day, see . . . then we met these chicks and we're kinda tapped for bread."

Sure, they'd been at the zoo all day — all that fresh air would've killed them.

" . . . so we phoned home and everything's cool, man. You'll get paid." He gave me the big smile again. Snoopy just sat back, watching, with eyes that were a hell of a lot older than the rest of him.

Suddenly I knew what was happening, and I didn't like any of it. I'd given them their chance to get out — it wouldn't work any better the second time. And Skinny wanted to talk. The subject wasn't encouraging:

"I guess you get some real weirdos in your cab, huh?"

"Yeah. Sometimes."

"I bet you take in a lot of bread in a night."

"Not that much. Why?"

"Nothin'. I just wondered."

He turned to whisper in Snoopy's ear, leaning far over the back of the seat. Snoopy watched me with those lizard eyes. Underfed, maybe, but this little creep was a long way from seventeen. The two of them snickered, then went back to their whispering.

As casually as I could, I took the microphone from the hook and laid it in my lap, half-expecting Skinny to grab it from me. But they hadn't noticed. Skinny turned to me again, and I wondered how many people had been suckered by that innocent smile.

"How much do you make in a night? A hunnert bucks?"

Good Jesus! The question was dumb enough the first time. What in hell was this kid stoned on? I hoped it wasn't speed—there are *no* rules when they're ripped on speed.

A driver can't carry a weapon—legally—no matter how hairy the district he works, nor how often he's been threatened, thumped, beaten, or stiffed. It's probably just as well; the business makes some guys a little paranoid, and I sometimes wondered about myself.

But there's always the radio. With luck, it can be a lot more useful than a tire iron or a timing-chain under the driver's seat—and nothing irritates a dispatcher more than the sound of an open mike. It roars through the office set in a blast of static and squeals, but you can't hear it in the car that's transmitting.

I pressed my thumb against the switch and held it for about ten seconds. When I released it the dispatcher's voice boomed into the car, angry: "Who's the clown playing with the radio?" I had his attention.

"Car ten-double-three clearing on Bright Street. That's ten-double-three, clearing in ten, thirty-four Bright." I tried to keep my voice light, almost sing-song, no panic. 1033 is the universal emergency number.

"Roger, ten-double-three. Call when you're clear." Donnie was a buddy of mine, and far from stupid. He'd know my voice; his own came through the radio just the way I wanted to hear it. Calm —and no questions.

"What the fuck was *that* all about?" Skinny wanted to know.

"The radio." I held the mike up for him to see. "We always tell the dispatcher where we're going. Just routine."

"Yeah? Hey, man! That's interesting! I bet you make a pile of money with that radio. All that money and all the broads . . ."

Good God! Where's the bottom line with this punk?

I said, "Look, my friend, forget what you're thinking. Don't you know we go to the garage every couple of hours . . . to turn in our money?"

Snoopy's grin in the mirror showed me how much he believed *that*.

We waited for a traffic light to change; I thought about running the next red one to catch come cop's attention, but there wasn't a cruiser in sight. It figured: any other night the streets would be crawling with them.

Skinny was still trying. "Aw, you got it all wrong, mister. We'll be home in a minute and you'll see . . ."

We pulled up in front of a peeling house on a street that was defeated fifty years ago. Even in the glare of the street lights it managed to be a dark, sullen place. I waited for them to make their move.

It didn't take long.

Skinny must have noticed the bulge in my shirt pocket. He reached across to grab the money and I felt Snoopy's arm around my throat, pulling me back against the seat. He was a lot stronger then he looked. I clutched at his arm with one hand and took a wild swing at Skinny with the other; my knuckles just grazed the side of his head as he dove for the door, yelling.

"Come on, Stu! Let's fuck off outa here! Now!"

Suddenly the pressure was gone from around my throat—but my arm felt funny. Hot.

"There's your receipt, sucker!" Snoopy's voice was shrill. I never did see the blade.

For a few seconds the street was full of the sound of running. A couple of doors slammed, far down the street. Then nothing.

I tried to reach for the door handle, but everything was slippery —and my arm wouldn't work. I was just able to grasp the mike with my other hand; it was like trying to reach across the Grand Canyon.

"Okay, Donnie . . . call them. I'm on Bright Street."

"They're on their way, guy. You all right?"

I don't remember answering. The car door flew open and the world's biggest cop leaned in. He looked beautiful.

"Christ!" He straightened and called to his partner, "Bring the box! Hurry!" Then to me, "Where'd he get you?"

"Right there, I think." I pointed to my left armpit. Things were beginning to slide away from me, like the feeling of a six-beer buzz. The other cop took an enormous bandage from the first-aid box and jammed it under my arm; he didn't have to tell me to hold it tight against me. There still wasn't any real pain, but my whole side was warm and sticky and the car seat was slick with blood.

I've never liked the sight of my own.

Those cops were pretty good—they didn't let me fall on my face as we walked the few hundred miles back to the cruiser. I have a fuzzy recollection of describing the two kids. And the Snoopy helmet on the one called Stu.

"Hell, that's Stu Wallace! We've been looking for that little bastard for weeks!"

I guess that's where I passed out.

☛ It's funny how much sleeping you can do in a hospital—and you never seem to catch up. You're free to do all the reading you've always wanted to do—and a half-dozen pages exhaust you.

Joan had put on a bright face to visit me, and seen to it that I had lots of smokes and lots to read. She smiled a lot; but the corners of her eyes were a little too tight. We talked, not about the things

I knew were on her mind; I think she was trying not to cry when she left.

If I had any sense I'd get out of this idiot business and marry that girl.

But, for now, it was enough to relax and enjoy all the attention. The pain came and went, but it wasn't too bad.

"How you doing, chief?"

I looked up from my book. It was one of the cops; the big one.

"Hey! It's good to see you!" It *was* good. I'm terrible with faces —and he was out of uniform—but you don't forget the guy who saves your butt. "You know — I don't even know your name? Officer...?"

"Harry. Harry will do just fine." He settled into a chair; and still looked enormous. "Say, you're lookin' pretty good!"

"Yeah. I feel pretty good. A few more days in here...I've got to thank you, you know..."

"Bullshit. I'm just glad we got there when we did. You were leaking like a busted barrel."

"Our dispatcher must've called..."

"Right...and he's a sharp lad. He knew right to the minute when you'd be there, and we didn't want to be sitting and waiting for you. Sometimes that just makes things worse...the sight of a cruiser can trigger a hell of a mess with some of these mean bastards."

"You got them?"

"Oh, yeah. Sure. I said they're mean, not smart. Those stupid sons of bitches ran right over to Stu's place, just a couple of blocks away. Another car picked them up while we were bringing you here. By the way, you got any idea who you tangled with?"

"No. Just a couple of punk kids..."

"Kids! Wallace is twenty-three and a borderline psycho. You're just lucky he didn't feel like using the gun."

"Gun...?"

"Yeah. He's done hard time on every weapons charge in the book, except murder...and one day he'll get around to that. He's a vicious little bastard, and his buddy's learning fast. Your luck could be worse, you know."

Suddenly I was very, very tired. I remembered the way Joan's eyes had looked.

I said, "I guess I'll have to lay charges . . ."

"Yeah. Well, we've already laid a wounding charge, but you'll have to follow through . . . identify them."

"Do I have a choice?" Fatigue came over me in great, rolling waves. I wanted off the whole goddam thing. I watched Harry's eyes take on that flat, steel look of the cop trying to keep his anger to himself.

He said, "Oh, you have a choice, all right. Just tell me you're willing to let murderous punks like that push you around . . . and we'll drop the charge. We've got enough on them to keep them busy for a while anyway. But I'm not going to give you any shit about duty or anything like that. Just think about it."

"Sure, officer. And you're right. But I'm so bloody tired . . ."

He rose to his enormous height and laid a meaty paw on my good shoulder. "I'll look in on you again. Take it easy, chief." He turned to leave.

"Oh. I damn near forgot. This belongs to you."

He handed me a wad of bills. "Count it," he said.

It was all there: the sixty-two dollars I'd had in my shirt pocket—and separate, held together with a paper-clip, two fives. "What's this?" I asked, holding up the two blue ones.

"Oh, that. Well, it took some persuading, but we got that from Stu's old man. Eight dollars for the fare—and a two-dollar tip for the driver."

His huge bulk filled the door as he walked out. Cops, I thought, some of them could be damn good friends. But it never happens.

Sleep came like a fall from a high place. Just before I went under, I knew I had to call Joan as soon as I woke up—it was time to talk about a few things.

And nobody's luck runs forever.

 EPILOGUE

☞ The fog had a funny smell about it: something between the aroma of roasting turkey and the brief, bitter stink of a match that didn't light properly.

The two of them strode through the fog toward the car, and the swirling stuff about their feet made them look as if they were walking a few inches off the ground. The one in red wore a goatee trimmed to a sharp point, and a strange head-covering — almost a cowl — that came low over his forehead. And his head looked lumpy. The one in white stood tall, but still managed to look stoop-shouldered, almost as if he wore a back-pack under his long white coat.

"Where to, gentlemen?"

"All the way, baby," Red said. "All the way." I didn't have to ask what he meant; I knew.

Whitey asked, "Is that all right with you, driver? We don't want to take you out of your way...."

I said, "I don't know. It's getting late. Maybe I should go home."

Red laughed. "Home? You'd go home...with the meter still ticking? I don't believe it!"

"Wait a minute!" Whitey said. "Maybe the driver has something else he'd rather do. Do you?"

I thought about it. "Well, there are one or two things..."

"Then drop us at the subway," Whitey said.

"Hold it, hold it!" Red said. "I say he's takin' us all the way. How about it, driver? Couldn't you use a trip like that?"

"But my shift'll be over by the time I get you there . . ."

"So? Everybody's got problems. What'll it be . . . yes or no?"

Whitey jumped in: "C'mon! Give the man a break! It's late, like he says, and I think he should go home. He must be beat from driving in this fog."

"Okay," Red said, "but I think he's makin' a mistake. It's an easy fare . . ."

I twisted up through the thick layers of sleep long enough to check the illuminated digital clock: another four hours before I'd. have to get up. It didn't take me ten seconds to fall back down again into oblivion. This time I was driving while a figure with a knife . . .

Suddenly: "Daddy! Daddy! Wake up, I need you!" The dear, familiar figure stood before me, back-lit by the sun, red-gold shafts of light glinting from her hair. "Don't do this any more, Dad. Please. It scares me!"

I was sweating.

Two coffees and a dozen cigarettes later I phoned the boss, and it was done. I haven't driven since.

But who knows? Who *ever* knows? Maybe I'll be back . . .